The Essential Guide to **London's Best Food Shops**

The Essential Guide to

London's Best Food Shops

Introduction by Antonio Carluccio

Photographs by Laura Forrester and John Freeman

NEW HOLLAND

This edition first published in 2006 by
New Holland Publishers (UK) Ltd
London • Cape Town • Sydney • Auckland
www.newhollandpublishers.com

Garfield House, 86–88 Edgware Road, London W2 2EA, United Kingdom

80 McKenzie Street, Cape Town 8001, South Africa

14 Aquatic Drive, Frenchs Forest, NSW 2086, Australia

218 Lake Road, Northcote, Auckland, New Zealand

1 3 5 7 9 10 8 6 4 2

ISBN 1 84537 291 3

Editor: Anne Konopelski
Researchers: Moya Gibbon, Brian Walker
Writers: Silvija Davidson, Susan Fleming, Sarah Freeman,
Beverly LeBlanc, Susan Wolk, Jo Younger

Photography: Laura Forrester, John Freeman
Design: Roger Hammond
Cartography: William Smuts
Illustrations: Madeleine David
Production: Hazel Kirkman

Editorial Direction: Rosemary Wilkinson

Reproduction by Pica Digital PTE Ltd, Singapore
Printed and bound by Kyodo Printing Co. Ltd

The Publishers have made every effort to ensure that the information contained in this
book is correct at the time of going to press. We cannot accept any liability for errors or
omissions or changes in the details given.

Front cover: A. Gold, Spitalfields
Back cover: The Spice Shop, Notting Hill (left) and Lina Stores, Soho (right)

❝ I like to buy the best food I can possibly afford, so that means seeking out the best producers and retailers.

If you know where to shop, London offers fantastic quality and choice. ❞

Henrietta Green

Contents

Introduction by Antonio Carluccio

THE BEST THING that can happen to someone newly arrived in Greater London, or even to a long-time resident, is to get to know which food shops are available.

I came to London 30 years ago as a wine merchant, a profession that took me all over the city visiting my customers – Italian restaurants and shops. I didn't have a guidebook like this at the time, but I still needed to get all sorts of ingredients to cook the authentic Italian food I had been preparing for my friends and myself in Europe. Consequently, I built up my own map of grocery shops, markets, and meat and fish shops where I could purchase the best ingredients. I always avoided supermarkets, because even then they only offered mediocre produce, which wasn't good enough for my cooking.

I purchased my groceries from Parmigiana, Lina Stores and I. Camisa; my beef from Bifulco or A. S. Portwine & Son; and my fish from Brewer Street. I also bought my fresh vegetables and fruit from Brewer Street, although they could never compare with the ripe fruit and other seasonal goods that I was used to finding in Italy.

It was five years later, when I decided to become a restaurateur, that my hunt for really high-quality Italian ingredients started in earnest. At this time, olive oils, good Parma ham, salami, cheeses and especially pasta were imported by a few Italians who wanted to start their own enterprises, while vegetables and fruit were delivered to London overnight. Good Italian wines have always been successful in the UK, since Italian wine makers understand that quality is always better than quantity.

In 1991, my wife and I decided to import our favourite Italian goods – those produced by specialist Italian artisans – and the first Carluccio's shop in Covent Garden was born. This was followed by many Carluccio's *caffés*/delicatessens/restaurants. Thanks to excellent management, Carluccio's has now grown to over 20 *caffés*, and we have managed to create a very successful business while still adhering to our philosophy of offering only the highest-quality, genuine Italian products.

In the last 20 years, London's food scene has changed beyond all recognition. There are more than 80 different types of cuisine on offer, which have made London the European capital of food. You can find shops and restaurants to suit any desire and taste here.

The city is also unique in that it imports original and authentic ingredients from all over the world, guaranteeing the ongoing production of ethnic foods. Small, specialist importers are ever expanding and invading the supermarket. This means it is now possible to gather everything from every corner of the world under one roof.

In my opinion, supermarkets have, unfortunately, destroyed many small, independent shops, monopolizing not only food but everything else. To compound matters, they rarely offer customers any of the experience, expertise or service that one would expect from a dedicated specialist.

Thanks to a range of movements, the organic production of vegetables and fruit, and the organic rearing of meat, have changed our food scene enormously in the last 20 years. The so-called Mediterranean diet has produced a healthier approach to food, and many artisanal products are now available at farmers' markets and specialist shops.

During my last visit to the Salone de Gusto, the Slow Food movement's biennial gastronomic food fair in Turin, thousands upon thousands of visitors demonstrated the importance of, and our growing respect for, traditionally crafted food stuffs. I was pleasantly surprised to see so many British exhibitors producing and selling artisanal goods of the highest quality, from beer to cheese to bacon and much more.

Terra Madre, which is endorsed by HRH The Prince of Wales, is a new food conference that is keen to defend small producers from the effects of globalization. There is still a lot to do, because masses of people in Britian are still confused about how to recognize good-quality food and how to buy it. This is easy to see when you look into the average family's shopping

trolley. Often, it's loaded with pre-made and packaged, processed food, instead of fresh ingredients.

The extremely successful campaign by Jamie Oliver, which showed how poorly school children are fed, is only one sign of the general low quality of food consumed by the biggest part of the population. Real education should start in schools, with part of the curriculum dedicated to domestic science. Equally, parents should be taught how to nourish their bodies and their families with healthy food.

All of the shopkeepers and market traders in this revised edition can help you to understand what good food is all about and show you how to cook it easily for your friends and family. Furthermore, a growing number of enterprising people are opening delicatessens that offer the best produce from Britain and abroad, and are replacing old-style corner shops.

I don't only shop for Italian food; my gastronomic curiousity has been titillated over the years by visiting foreign restaurants. I like to experiment and often visit Chinese and Japanese shops for their exotic, fresh produce. Living in London is like having the entire culinary world at your feet – so do take advantage of it.

Happy hunting and *buon appetito*,

About this guide

THIS UNIQUE GUIDE is for people who love good food at all levels – from haute cuisine, French or Italian cooking to ethnic peasant dishes. We aim to guide readers to the best retail suppliers in Greater London. We tell you where to go to buy high-quality ingredients from knowledgeable staff who are passionate about what they do. We have also included our (doubtless controversial) list of the food shops that we would single out as the very best in London (page 12).

In the course of our research, we have visited hundreds of retailers and dozens of markets. Our decision to include a particular entry is based on the quality of the produce on offer, its diversity, the knowledge and enthusiasm of the people running the shop or store, plus the service it provides in areas where high-quality food outlets are rarer than may be the case in central London.

So, while on a superficial level it may seem a little strange that a book claiming to be the essential guide to London's best food shops includes food halls ranging in style (and price) from Harvey Nichols to Wing Yip – or from Luigi's or Mortimer & Bennett to Talad Thai, Green Street Market and Borough Market – in truth, such a broad selection is completely valid to today's discerning cook or food shopper.

In many cases, the shops also sell wines and spirits, but food has been our focus for this book. The trend towards food-to-go (also known as *traiteur* food or takeaway dishes) is on the increase – a much-needed boon for the busy urban cook. Catering is on a wider scale than before and is offered by many of these outlets.

LONDON'S AREAS

This guide divides London into seven sections: Central, City and East, West, North-West, North-East, South-East and South-West.

At the beginning of each section, a map gives a geographical reference to the areas covered. The entries are arranged alphabetically by neighbourhood. Interspersed among the shop entries are relevant quotes from food personalities, various food features and information about cookery-related shops in the area. The stylized maps, which should be used with a good London street atlas, give a general overview to the areas covered. They are not intended to give fine detail.

THE ENTRIES
At the top of each main entry, you will find the full name of the shop, its address, including post code, telephone and fax numbers, followed by details on opening and closing hours, public transport and payment. Symbols alongside each entry provide at-a-glance information about specialities.

THE PHOTOGRAPHS
The photographs show a selection of shops and markets that are particularly photogenic and illustrate the diversity of outlets all over London. They are not an indicator of hierarchy.

FARMERS' MARKETS
Farmers' markets are listed in a section at the back of the book. The number of farmers' markets in London is growing all the time, and locations and times can and do change. For more information, please telephone 020 7704 9659 or visit www.lfm.org.uk.

MAIL-ORDER & DELIVERY SERVICES
London-based businesses that are exclusively mail order have been listed at the back of the book, in a separate section. Their food is either sent by post or delivered, and in some cases you have the option to go and collect it yourself. Shops that offer mail-order services have been listed in the main part of the guide, and this has been indicated; they are not listed in the mail-order section.

INDEX
At the end of the book, there is a general index of all shops, listed alphabetically, and one of all the mail-order and delivery services, also listed alphabetically. There is also an index of shops listed under specialities, and the index for grocers delicatessens has been further subdivided into various national specialities.

READER FEEDBACK
We are constantly updating our information, so do let us know your opinions about new shops or other information that you think should be included in the next edition.

Alternatively, if you are a shop and you think you should be reviewed for inclusion in a future edition, please contact us.

Anne Konopelski, Editor
E-mail: postmaster@nhpub.co.uk

Best in town

BY NATIONALITY

 BRITISH
Fortnum & Mason 46
A. Gold 67
Hope and Greenwood 162
Melrose and Morgan 128

 FRENCH
Comptoir Gascon 61
Truc Vert 44
Villandry 32

 GREEK
T. Adamou & Sons 74
Athenian Grocery 16

 INDIAN
V. B. & Sons 134
Wembley Exotics Ltd 135

 ITALIAN
Carluccio's 28
G. Gazzano & Sons 62
Lina Stores 53
Luigi's 24
Stefano Cavallini 175
Tavola 106
Valentina 181

 JAPANESE
Atari-Ya 119

 JEWISH
Panzer's 133

 MIDDLE EASTERN
Green Valley 38
Le Maroc 102
Reza Pâtisserie 94
Super Bahar 94

 PORTUGUESE
Lisboa Delicatessen 103

 SOUTH-EAST ASIAN
Loon Fung 27
Talad Thai 183
Wing Yip 117

 SPANISH
Brindisa 60
R. Garcia & Sons 98

 TURKISH
Yasar Halim 140

BY TYPE OF SHOP

 **BAKERIES**

Baker & Spice 20
& Clarke's 92
De Gustibus 36
Konditor & Cook 156
Lighthouse Bakery 176
Poilâne 19

 BUTCHERS

Butcher & Edmonds 66
Frank Godfrey 141
Freeman's Butchers 118
The Ginger Pig 38
Kingsland Butchers 101
C. Lidgate 89
Randalls 86

 CHEESE SHOPS

La Fromagerie 141
Neal's Yard Dairy 31
Paxton & Whitfield 48

 CHOCOLATE

L'Artisan du Chocolat 18
Rococo 25
Theobroma Cacao 79

 COFFEE SHOPS

Algerian Coffee Stores 50
A. Angelucci 51
H. R. Higgins (Coffee-man) 42
Monmouth Coffee Company 30

 DELICATESSENS

East Dulwich Deli 161
Gusto & Relish 170
Mortimer & Bennett 78

 FISHMONGERS

Aberdeen Sea Products 155
Chalmers & Gray 95
Condon Fishmongers 179
Cope's Seafood 82
Covent Garden Fishmongers 76
H.S. Linwood & Sons 59
Sandys 189
Steve Hatt 146

 FOOD HALLS

Harrods 33
Harvey Nichols 34

 GREENGROCERS

Andreas Georghiou & Co. 75
Michanicou Brothers 90
The Olive Tree 126

 MARKETS

Borough Market 157

 PÂTISSERIES

Bagatelle Boutique 54
Maison Blanc 132

 SPICES, HERBS AND OILS

The Spice Shop 106

 WHOLEFOOD AND ORGANIC SHOPS

Fresh & Wild 97
Oliver's Wholefood Store 182
Planet Organic 16

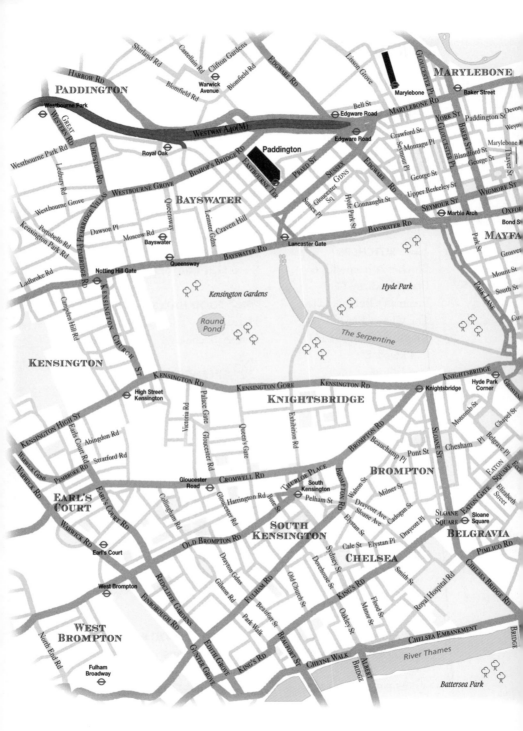

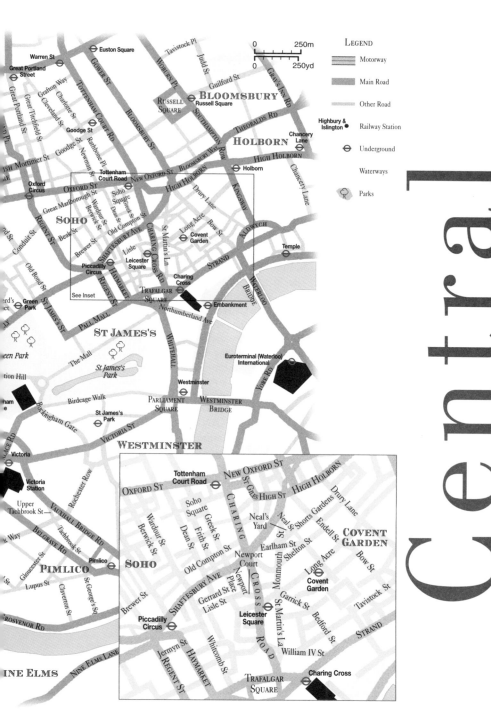

Bayswater

Greek
Cypriot
Grocer
Delicatessen

★ ATHENIAN GROCERY
16A Moscow Road,
London W2 4BT
Tel: 020 7229 6280
Open: Mon-Sat 8.30am-7pm,
Sun 9.30am-1pm, Bank holidays
10am-1pm **Closed:** 25, 26 Dec.
Tube: Bayswater, Queensway
Bus: 70 **Payment:** cash, cheque

Just down the road from the
Greek Orthodox Cathedral, this
corner shop is painted in the
blue and white colours of the
Greek flag. Manager Kimon
Kyprianides proudly explains
how Greeks and Greek Cypriots
come from all over London and
the south-east to shop here on
weekdays, and from as far away
as Scotland on weekends.
Friendly assistants readily give
advice. Try the Greek delight or
crisp Lebanese flatbread, or,
when you don't feel like
cooking, go for the ready meals,
which include stuffed vine
leaves, olive turnovers and
baklava. The shop carries a wide
range of seasonal produce
(grapefruit-sized quinces, figs,
pomegranates and cactus fruit in
early autumn, and bunches of
bitter endive in summer), as well
as the best of Eastern
Mediterranean foods. You'll
find loose feta, fresh filo,
halloumi, taramasalata, olive
oils, more than 12 types of
loose olive mixes, breadsticks,
freshly baked bread, coffee
and good-value bunches of
salad greens.

MARKUS COFFEE CO.
13 Connaught Street,
London W2 2AY
Tel/Fax: 020 7723 4020
Website: www.markuscoffee.com
Open: Mon-Fri 9am-5.30pm, Sat
9am-1pm **Closed:** Sun, Bank
holidays **Tube:** Marble Arch
Bus: 6, 7, 15, 16, 16a, 17, 23, 36, 98
Payment: cash, cheque, Amex,
Delta, Maestro, MasterCard, Visa
**Catalogue, delivery, mail order,
retail and wholesale**

Coffee

Established in 1957, this
specialist shop offers 22
different blends and roasts on
the premises every day. You'll
also find a selection of coffee-
making equipment, including
espresso makers and plungers,
and a wide range of sugars,
biscuits and tea.

★ PLANET ORGANIC
42 Westbourne Grove,
London W2 5SH
Tel: 020 7727 2227
Mail-order tel: 020 7221 1345
Email: deliveries@
planetorganic.com **Website:**
www.planetorganic.com
Open: Mon-Sat 9.30am-8.30pm,
Sun 12pm-6pm **Closed:** some
Bank holidays **Tube:** Bayswater,
Royal Oak **Bus:** 7, 23, 27, 70
Payment: cash, cheque, Amex,
Delta, Maestro, Visa
Delivery, mail order, food-to-go

Wholefood
Organic
Food Hall

This large, airy shop is the
flagship of the three-strong
Planet Organic chain, which
prides itself on having
established the UK's first

organic supermarket. There's a strong community feel here – the staff is friendly, and there is a pleasing bustle about the place. Although not all of the stock is organic, a large part of it is – including the vegetables, fruit, fresh meat and fish, eat-in and takeaway hot dishes and salads, cheeses, dairy products, tinned and jarred products, wines and beers – and the quality is excellent and as natural as possible. The store carries a wide range of pasta, rice and grains, including gluten-, wheat-, yeast- and dairy-free products. You'll also find books, pet foods, health and beauty products and supplements (with beauty and nutrition advice to boot), and can enjoy an organic coffee or freshly made fruit juice while you browse. Delivery is by bicycle for those who live within a four-mile radius.

Branches: see Fitzrovia, page 32, and Fulham, page 85

South-East Asian Grocer

TAWANA
18-20 Chepstow Road,
London W2 5BD
Tel: 020 7221 6316
Open: every day, including Bank holidays, 9.30am-8pm **Tube:** Bayswater, Notting Hill Gate
Bus: 7, 28, 31, 70, 328 **Payment:** cash, cheque

This compact South-East Asian grocery specializes in Thai ingredients but also has a good selection of items from China, Malaysia, Indonesia, Korea, Singapore, Japan and the Philippines. Thai fresh fruit, herbs and vegetables such as jackfruit, lychees, rambutans, grass jelly, sugar cane and fresh young coconut are imported directly every Wednesday and Saturday. Look out for fresh kaffir lime leaves, galangal and lemongrass, as well as purple yams, banana leaves, chok fui and Thai basil. The extensive range of dried fish includes mackerel, tiny anchovies, squid and shrimps, while the frozen fish counter is stocked with abalone, shrimps, squid and prawns, plus fish from the Mekong Valley in China. You can also buy freshly made rice, noodles and tofu, and several varieties of ready-made pastes.

Branch: see Plaistow, page 148

Belgravia

★ **BAKER & SPICE**
54-56 Elizabeth Street,
London SW1W 9PB
Tel: 020 7730 3033

Main shop and branch: see Chelsea, page 20

Bakery
Delicatessen
Pâtisserie

Chocolate

THE CHOCOLATE SOCIETY
36 Elizabeth Street,
London SW1W 9NZ
Tel: 020 7259 9222
Mail-order tel: 0845 2308899
Fax: 020 7259 9666
Website: www.chocolate.co.uk
Open: Mon-Fri 9.30am-5.30pm,
Sat 9.30am-4pm **Closed:** Sun,
Bank holidays **Tube:** Victoria,
Sloane Square **Bus:** C1 **Payment:**
cash, cheque, Delta, Maestro,
MasterCard, Visa
**Catalogue, café, catering,
delivery, gift service, mail order**

The shelves are packed with
real drinking chocolate, sauces,
truffles and biscuits in this
delightful shop. Chocolate bars
include the full Valrhona range;
own-label 40%, 64%, 66%,
70% and 100% cocoa solids
styles; and one variety made
from pure Criollo cocoa beans.
The shop, which also operates
as a café, is the public face of
the Chocolate Society and its
manufacturing and mail-order
service, which is based in North
Yorkshire. Join the society for
£70 to receive a badge, a
hamper of chocolates and a
discount on mail order.

Branch: see Mayfair, page 42

JEROBOAMS
50-52 Elizabeth Street,
London SW1W 9PB
Tel: 020 7730 8108

Main shop: see Holland Park,
page 88

Cheese Shop
Delicatessen

> ❝More and more people
> care about what they eat and
> how it is actually produced.
> Once again, they are
> indulging in the pleasure of
> good food and are no longer
> assuming that to be good it
> must therefore be foreign. ❞
>
> HRH The Prince of Wales

★ L'ARTISAN DU CHOCOLAT
89 Lower Sloane Street,
London SW1W 8DA
Tel: 020 7824 8365
Fax: 020 7730 6139
Website:
www.artisanduchocolat.com
Open: Mon-Sat 10am-7pm,
Sun 12am-5pm
Tube: Sloane Square
Bus: 11, 137, 211, 360
Mainline station: Victoria
Payment: cash, cheque, Amex,
Delta, MasterCard, Maestro,
Visa
Mail order

Chefs and food writers routinely
rave about the chocolates
produced by this small, family-
run business. Gordon Ramsay,
who carries them in his

Chocolate

restaurants, has even called them 'the Bentley of chocolate'. Each day, owner Gerard Coleman whips up fresh batches by hand in his atelier just outside London, using only the finest, GM- and preservative-free ingredients. The resulting confections, with their intense flavours, instantly betray his background as a chef. You'll find thick, burnished slabs of chocolate, delicate Moroccan mint thins and *feuillantines* (almond and hazelnut pralines), and individual pieces in flavours ranging from violet to green cardamom. Most popular are the liquid salted caramel truffles, although the hanging balls and rainforest eggs, adorned with transfers of jungle vegetation, also fly off the shelves at Christmas and Easter. The shop's flawless presentation make it a joy to browse here – and you might even find yourself rubbing shoulders with L'Artisan du Chocolat fans Cilla Black and Joan Collins.

French Pâtisserie

PÂTISSERIE VALERIE

17 Motcomb Street,
London SW1X 8LB
Tel: 020 7245 6161

Main shop and branches: see Soho, page 54

French Bakery

★ POILÂNE

46 Elizabeth Street,
London SW1W 9PA
Tel: 020 7808 4910
Fax: 020 7808 4920

Website: www.poilane.fr
Open: Mon-Fri 7.30am-7.30pm, Sat 7.30am-6pm **Closed:** Sun, some Bank holidays **Tube:** Victoria, Sloane Square **Bus:** C1
Payment: cash, cheque, Delta, Maestro, MasterCard, Visa

The first thing that strikes you as you enter this delightful bakery is the smell – it is unmistakeably French. This is no ordinary French bakery, however. Pierre Poilâne opened his first shop in 1932 in the Saint Germain des Prés district of Paris, making bread with stone-ground flour, natural fermentation and a wood-fired oven. All of the traditional bread-making methods are used here. The large, round loaves are baked on the premises in an oven that is based on an ancient Roman design. In addition to the very distinctive Poilâne bread (each loaf is marked with a large 'P'), there are rye loaves, walnut bread, and currant and raisin bread, as well as perfect croissants and other pâtisserie. The shop also sell its own flour, sugar and sea salt from Guérande – the same ingredients used in its loaves.

Bloomsbury

APOSTROPHE

216-217 Tottenham Court Road, London W1T 7PT
Tel: 020 7436 6688

Main shop and branches: see Oxford Street, page 43

French Bakery

Bakery

BLOOMSBURY CHEESES
61B Judd Street,
London WC1H 9QT
Tel/Fax: 020 7387 7645
Open: Mon-Fri 10am-7pm, Sat
10am-5.30pm **Closed:** Sun, Bank
holidays **Tube:** King's Cross,
Russell Square **Bus:** 10, 30, 68,
73, 91, 168, 188 **Mainline
station:** King's Cross **Payment:**
cash, cheque, Delta, Electron,
Maestro, MasterCard, Solo,
Visa

Everything in this beautifully
designed shop is both pristine
and perfectly presented, from
the Crottins in glass-covered
wooden boxes, to the glass
bowls filled with glistening
olives, and the bags of pasta
shapes hanging from the pink-
washed walls. Among the
enticements is a selection of
chargrilled, bottled vegetables,
principally from Seggiano,
which also produces the honeys
and seasonal *panforte* and
panettone. The own-label extra
virgin olive oil from Crete;
Poilâne sourdough, rye and
walnut loaves; and The
Chocolate Society confections
are as carefully chosen as the
cheeses and other dairy
products. So, too, is the
cider and ale, and the 30-
strong range of wines
supplied by Les Caves de
Pyrène. All of the bottles
come complete with
tasting notes and cheese-
matching suggestions.

★ KONDITOR & COOK
46 Gray's Inn Road,
London W1D 5DY
Tel: 020 7404 6300

Main shop and branches: see
Borough, page 156

Chelsea

★ BAKER & SPICE
47 Denyer Street,
London SW3 2LX
Tel: 020 7589 4734
Fax: 020 7823 9148
Website:
www.bakerandspice.co.uk
Open: Mon-Sat 7am-7pm, Sun
8.30am-5pm (reduced hours on
Bank holidays) **Closed:** 3 weeks
in August, 1 week at Christmas
Tube: Knightsbridge, South
Kensington **Bus:** 14, 49, 74, 345,
C1 **Payment:** cash, cheque,
Delta, Maestro, Visa
Catering, food-to-go

This popular bakery-cum-
traiteur was established by Gail
Mejia in 1995, though its two
gigantic brick baking ovens, still
miraculously operating with
only a few modifications, date
from 1902. All of the shop's
food is baked here daily and
nightly. The sourdough loaves,
some flavoured with
caramelized garlic, some with
potato and rosemary, are Baker
& Spice's speciality, but you'll
also find wonderful filled
croissants, croque monsieur,
Parmesan and pistachio biscuits,
foot-long cheese straws, muffins,

Bakery
Pâtisserie

Bakery
Delicatessen
Pâtisserie

Danish pastries, chocolate fudge and carrot cakes, and fig, plum or pear tarts. The food-to-go includes a range of fresh salads with beetroot, cucumbers, tomatoes and peppers – plus roasted peppers and fresh mozzarella salad. Baker & Spice also stocks its own range of home-made jams, coffee and olive oils.

Branches: see Belgravia, page 17, and Queens Park, page 129

Fishmonger

BIBENDUM CRUSTACEA
Michelin House, 81 Fulham Road, London SW3 6RD
Tel: 020 7589 0864
Open: Tues-Sat 9am-5pm
Closed: Sun, Mon **Tube:** South Kensington **Bus:** 14, 49, 345
Payment: cash, cheque, Amex, Delta, Maestro, MasterCard, Visa
Bespoke delivery, catering, food-to-go

This smart fish and shellfish counter sits in the forecourt of the Michelin building. It's renowned for its Saturday-morning lobster sale – when you can buy a beautifully cooked and dressed 1-lb Maine lobster – but you'll also find top-quality products from across the British Isles, including Colchester oysters, langoustines from Scotland's west coast and diver-caught scallops from Guernsey.

★ CARLUCCIO'S
236 Fulham Road,
London SW10 9NB
Tel: 020 7376 5960

Main shop and branches: see Covent Garden, page 28

THE CITY MEAT
421 Kings Road,
London SW10 0LR
Tel/Fax: 020 7352 9894
Open: Mon-Sat 8.30am-6pm
Closed: Sun, Bank holidays
Tube: Sloane Square **Bus:** 11, 22,
Payment: cash, cheque, Delta, Maestro, MasterCard, Visa

An unprepossessing name belies the quality of the produce sold here. More than just a butcher, this shop operates both as a delicatessen and a purveyor of high-quality meat and game (both fur and feather). It sells baby lamb, suckling pig, kid and Spanish foie gras to order in season, plus bronze turkeys and free-range geese at Christmas. The meat counter includes *albondigas* (meatballs made with veal and pork), which are made daily on the premises, as well as marinated chicken and lamb kebabs in summer. Around Christmas, you'll find high-quality Serrano ham and Lacon Gallego (cured shoulder of pork on the bone). There are also delicious Spanish sausages, more than 70 cheeses, a plethora of dried, tinned and packeted goods, and jars of preserves from France, Spain, and Italy.

Italian
Delicatessen
Café

Butcher
Game dealer
Spanish
Delicatessen

Gourmet
Delicatessen

FINNS OF CHELSEA GREEN

4 Elystan Street,
London SW3 3NS
Tel: 020 7225 0733/4
Open: Mon-Fri 8am-5.30pm, Sat 8am-1pm **Closed:** Sun, Bank holidays **Tube:** Sloane Square, South Kensington **Bus:** 11, 14, 19, 22, 49, 211, 319, 345
Payment: cash, cheque, Delta, Maestro, MasterCard, Visa
Catalogue, catering, food-to-go

Julia Bannister runs this food and catering business from a small, uncluttered shop. It has a good selection of olives, pickles, a variety of salts and a few South African specialities. The principal line, though, is the food-to-go, which is cooked daily in the kitchen behind the shop, using top-quality ingredients. The catalogue lists a range of favourites that might be on offer depending on season and availability of ingredients, including hot and cold soups, wonderful salads, grilled and roasted vegetables, a selection of hot and cold meat and poultry dishes, sandwiches and desserts. Finns prepares hot and cold canapés to enhance your drinks parties, and will also put together picnics. Service is friendly, helpful and discreet.

Party cakes

JANE ASHER PARTY CAKES & SUGERCRAFT

22-24 Cale Street,
London SW3 3QU
Tel: 020 7584 6177

Fax: 020 7584 6179
Website: www.jane-asher.co.uk
Open: Mon-Sat 9.30am-5.30pm
Closed: Sun, Bank holidays **Tube:** South Kensington, Sloane Square **Bus:** 11, 14, 19, 22, 211, 319 **Payment:** cash, cheque, Amex, Delta, Maestro, MasterCard, Visa
Mail order

This cake shop sells over 2,000 cakes a year, all made to order on the premises. Clients can specify the design or choose from a portfolio of more than 5,000 ideas that can be transformed into edible fantasies – from a Gucci shoe or Prada handbag to a Van Gogh self-portrait. Allow 10 days for a simpler idea and two months for a wedding cake. The shop also provides everything you are ever likely to need for decorating a cake yourself – including nozzles, cake boards, cutters and moulds, recipe books and candles, plus hard-to-find items such as black food colouring and edible gold leaf. Personalized cakes can be delivered anywhere in the country by courier.

LA BOTTEGA DEL SOLE

323 Fulham Road,
London SW10 9QL
Tel: 020 7351 7370
Fax: 020 7351 7319
Website:
www.labottegadelsole.com
Open: Mon-Sat 8.30am-9pm,
Sun 11am-5pm
Tube: Fulham Broadway, South

Italian
Delicatessen
Traiteur

Kensington **Bus:** 14, 211, 328, 414, C3 **Mainline station:** West Brompton **Payment:** cash, cheque, Amex, Delta, MasterCard, Maestro, Visa **Catering, food-to-go, delivery (free for orders above £10 and within the borough of Kensington and Chelsea, but a £3 charge applies to all other orders), cakes to order**

Former investment banker Patricia Hamzahee has brought a little bit of *la dolce vita* to Chelsea with this delightful deli/*traiteur*. Downstairs, the in-house kitchen churns out a daily-changing menu of seasonal dishes from across Italy. On our visit, grilled aubergines and beef marinated in Balsamic vinegar jostled for counter space with handmade pasta, salads and desserts including a tempting ricotta and chocolate crumb cake. The shop is designed for 'busy people who love to cook but don't have the time and don't want to compromise', says Hamzahee. 'We provide freshly cooked food using high-quality ingredients. It's all prepared the way you'd make it at home.' Bespoke sandwiches can be made on the spot from the shop's wide range of Italian cured meats and cheeses. Or, if you're feeling inspired to do some home cooking, you can choose from the abundant wines, olive oils, sauces and pasta – Setaro's gluten-free *farro*, or spelt, pasta is especially popular – which are sourced from specialist Italian producers. La Bottega del Sole also stocks beautifully hand-crafted Murano glassware and multicoloured ceramic earthenware for those keen to create a truly authentic *cucina di casa Italiana*.

LA MARÉE

Fishmonger

76 Sloane Avenue,
London SW3 3DZ
Tel: 020 7589 8067
Open: Mon-Sat 8am-6pm
Closed: Sun, Bank holidays
Tube: South Kensington **Bus:** 14, 49, 345 **Payment:** cash, cheque, Amex, Delta, Maestro, MasterCard, Visa
Catering, food-to-go

This tiny shop, which is owned and run by neighbouring restaurant Poissonnerie de l'Avenue's proprietor Peter

HANSENS KITCHEN EQUIPMENT

306 Fulham Road, London SW10 9ER
Tel: 020 7351 6933
Website: www.hansens.co.uk

In the Area This shop and design consultancy, which is also known as The Chefs Shop, is aimed at professionals but will appeal to serious amateur cooks, too. Hansens designs and supplies top kitchens around the country and abroad for clients including Claridge's, The Parisienne Chop House and The Embassy. You'll also find state-of-the-art premier range cookers here, as well as espresso machines, heavy-duty mincers and stainless-steel tables.

Rosignoli, sells top-quality fish and shellfish. You'll find a variety of sea fish in season, plus oysters, scallops, crabs, lobster, four types of Iranian caviar, smoked salmon, eel, mackerel and cod's roe. Staff will prepare and cook whole fish or portions to order, and there are always some home-made sauces, including tartare, dill, rouille or hollandaise, to go with your fish.

Italian
Delicatessen

★ LUIGI'S

349 Fulham Road,
London SW10 9TW
Tel: 020 7352 7739
Open: Mon-Fri 9am-9.30pm, Sat 9am-7pm **Closed:** Sun, Bank holidays **Tube:** Fulham Broadway **Bus:** 14, 211, 345, 414
Payment: cash, cheque, Amex, Delta, Maestro, MasterCard, Visa
Catering, food-to-go

Owned by Luigi Molinaro from Montecatini in Tuscany, and run with the help of his daughter, Selina, this well-established shop is one of the best Italian delis in town in terms of quality and breadth of stock and service. It has a deservedly large and loyal local customer base. The window display boasts fresh bread including *pugliese,* ciabatta, corn bread, focaccia and the like, plus seasonal fruit, vegetables and herbs. Inside, the cheese counter contains well over a dozen types of pecorino, smoked mozzarella di bufala, *scamorza* and the other, more common Italian cheeses. The food-to-go range, cooked on the premises, is fabulous – you'll find boned, stuffed and roasted Italian chickens, home-made soups (minestrone is a speciality), roasted meat, cooked sauces and roasted vegetables. Luigi's home-made pasta sauces include a sensational porcini sauce. The deli meat counter is similarly impressive, with more unusual hams such as Carpegna Prosciutto San Leo and San Daniele Reserva (cured for 18 months), as well as a big range of salume, speck, bresaola, smoked pancetta and *lardo salato* (salted lard for cooking). Towards the back is the freshly made pasta, which includes delicious ravioli stuffed with mushrooms and herbs, and trays of marinated, roasted and grilled vegetables including artichokes, peppers, mushrooms, garlic and courgettes. The floor-to-ceiling shelving on all sides of the shop groans with dried pasta, Italian coffee cakes, biscuits and preserves. We saw lovely jars of *baba Positanesi* – tiny rum *babas* preserved in lemon liqueur, a speciality of Positano. You'll also find organic Italian ice cream, a selection of wines and an interesting range of liqueurs and *amari.*

French
Bakery
Pâtisserie

★ MAISON BLANC

11 Elystan Street,
London SW3 3NT
Tel: 020 7584 6913

303 Fulham Road, London
SW10 9QH
Tel: 020 7795 2663

Main shop and branches: see
St John's Wood, page 132

– but its emphasis is more on offering good-quality items sourced from reliable suppliers. The shop has its own range of pickles, jams, sauces and pasta, and some fresh bread is baked on the premises daily. It's famous for its hampers – but if you prefer to eat on-site, the café serves a range of hot and cold food and drinks.

Delicatessen
Greengrocer
Organic

PARTRIDGES

2-5 Duke of York Square,
London SW3 4LY
Tel: 020 7730 0651/7102
Fax: 020 7730 7104
Website: www.partridges.co.uk
Open: Mon-Sun 8am-10pm
Closed: 25, 26 Dec. **Tube:** Sloane
Square **Bus:** 11, 19, 22, 49, 211,
319 **Payment:** cash, cheque,
Amex, Delta, Maestro,
MasterCard, Visa
**Free delivery, bespoke hampers
and picnics, catering**

This upmarket delicatessen and off-licence has been in business for over 32 years and has established itself as a purveyor of high-quality food from around the world. It is, in fact, almost like a very smart, miniature supermarket, with everything from baked beans to the finest caviar. The shop stocks over 7,000 items, and Amit Jain, the in-store buyer, is always looking out for newer and more unusual foods. The fresh fruit and vegetables are all organic, as is the fresh meat. Partridges also stocks organic alternatives to most of its store-cupboard items

★ ROCOCO

321 Kings Road,
London SW3 5EP
Tel: 020 7352 5857
Fax: 020 7352 7360
Website:
www.rococochocolates.com
Open: Mon-Sat 10am-6.30pm,
Sun 12pm-5pm **Tube:** South
Kensington, Sloane Square **Bus:**
11, 19, 22, 49, 211, 319, 345
Payment: cash, cheque, Amex,
Delta, Electron, JCB, Maestro,
MasterCard, Solo, Visa
Catalogue, mail order

This shop, heaven for chocoholics, is stacked from floor to ceiling with confections, many of which are produced in Rococo's south-east London kitchens. The huge range of chocolate bars includes more than 25 flavoured, organic artisan bars packaged in trademark tobacco pouches. Don't leave without trying the basil and Persian lime, lavender or chilli pepper – or the best-selling orange and geranium in dark chocolate or sea salt in milk chocolate. The highlight of the foiled bar range is the

Chocolate
Organic

Grenada Chocolate Company's 70% cocoa organic bar, which is wholly produced on a single estate on the Caribbean island. You'll also find boxed and packaged chocolates, a fine selection of French and Italian confectionary and – on Valentine's Day and at Easter – sought-after hand-painted hearts and eggs.

Branch: see Marylebone, page 41

Butcher
Game Dealer

WYNDHAM HOUSE
339 Fulham Road,
London SW10 9TW
Tel: 020 7352 7888
Open: Mon-Fri 8am-6.30pm, Sat 8am-5.30pm **Closed:** Sun
Tube: Fulham Broadway, South Kensington **Bus:** 14, 211, 328, 414, C3 **Mainline station:** West Brompton **Payment:** cash, cheque, Delta, MasterCard, Maestro, Visa

Poultry farmer Lee Mullett's Borough Market stand has been so successful in recent years that he launched this standalone butcher's shop in 2004. It naturally stocks Mullett's chicken, but you'll also find organic, free-range pork and chicken from Dorset's Childhay Manor Farm, Pembrokeshire free-range lamb including prized salt marsh lamb in the summer, beef, rabbit, duck and a full range of bacon, sausages and burgers. Customers return again and again for the generous cuts of meat, but the prepared dishes are also

extremely popular. Be sure to try the superb beef and chicken stir-fries, duck grottin (three duck breasts filled with orange zest and tied as a roasting joint) and chicken parcels stuffed with foie gras.

Chinatown

GOLDEN GATE GROCERS
100 Shaftesbury Avenue,
London W1
Tel: 020 7437 0014
Tel: 020 7287 3254
Open: Mon-Sun 10am-7.45pm
Closed: Bank holidays **Tube:** Leicester Square **Bus:** 14, 19, 22, 24, 29, 38, 176 **Payment:** cash, cheque, Maestro, MasterCard, Visa

Chinese
Grocer
Greengrocer

This shop sells mainly Chinese groceries, though it also stocks a good range of South-East Asian spice pastes. It's a major stockist of exotic fruit such as durian, mangosteen, longans, lychees and carambola – and also seasonal tropical vegetables including green carrots, ridged gourds, bitter melons, Taiwanese bok-choy and many other fabulously named greens. The friendly staff are more than happy to help you to identify unfamiliar fruit and vegetables.

Chinese
Food Hall

★ LOON FUNG

42-44 Gerrard
Street, London
W1D 5QG
Tel: 020 7437 7332
Fax: 020 7439 1585
Open: Mon-Sun 10am-8pm
Closed: Bank holidays **Tube:**
Leicester Square **Bus:** 14, 19, 22,
24, 29, 38, 176 **Payment:** cash,
cheque, Maestro (£5 minimum),
MasterCard, Visa

This Chinese food hall has a resident butcher, but pork and pork spare parts are the only meats available. Chinese butchers cut pork differently than their British counterparts, so you'll get spare ribs and streaky belly slices with the correct ratio of fat and meat. Offal including spleen, heart, lungs and even coagulated blood is available, as it is integral to much Chinese cooking. There's a wide range of processed fish products, including dried shrimps, fish balls and cakes, squid balls and shellfish. Frozen fish and shellfish are imported, as are rare vegetables and fruit such as kumquats and galangal. A separate section stocks a variety of spice pastes, dry noodles, flours, sauces, canned pickles, dried spices and Chinese utensils

Branches: see Tottenham, page 150, Wembley, page 134

NEW LOON MOON

9A Gerrard Street,
London W1D 5PL
Tel: 020 7734 3887
Fax: 020 7439 8880
Open: Mon-Sun 10.30am-8pm
Closed: 25, 26 Dec. **Tube:**
Leicester Square **Bus:** 14, 19, 22,
24, 29, 38, 176 **Mainline station:**
Charing Cross **Payment:** cash,
cheque, Amex, Delta, Maestro,
MasterCard, Visa
Bespoke delivery

Situated right across from Loon Fung in Gerrard Street, this little food hall boldly advertises that it specializes in Malaysian, Chinese, Filipino, Indonesian, Japanese, Korean, Singaporean and Thai products. And it delivers on that promise, for it is the best place for such esoterics as Thai fresh fruit and vegetables, pandan leaves, Filipino spice pastes and pickles, processed Thai curry pastes, a wide range of tofu products, Korean kimchee, Malaysian sambals and korma pastes, and Japanese miso soup and sushi.

South-East
Asian
Grocer
Greengrocer

Chinese
Grocer
Greengrocer

NEWPORT SUPERMARKET

28-29 Newport Court,
London WC2H 7PQ
Tel: 020 7437 2386
Open: Mon-Sun 10.30am-8pm
Closed: 25, 26 Dec. **Tube:**
Leicester Square **Bus:** 14, 19, 22,
24, 29, 38, 176 **Payment:** cash

This, basically a scaled-down
version of Loon Fung (page 27),
is the smallest of Chinatown's
food shops. Like the others, it
has a wide range of Chinese
canned vegetables and fruit,
pickles, snacks and biscuits.
It also stocks unusual items
such as pickled bamboo
shoots, fresh tropical fruit
and vegetables, herbs and
other flavourings.

Chinese
Vietnamese
Grocer
Greengrocer

SEE WOO HONG

18-20 Lisle Street,
London WC2H 7BD
Tel: 020 7439 8325,
020 7734 4468
Open: Mon-Sun 10am-7.45pm
Closed: 25 Dec. **Tube:** Leicester
Square **Bus:** 14, 19, 24, 29, 38,
176 **Payment:** cash, cheque,
Delta, Electron, Maestro

With a purple façade and no
visible English name, this shop
is similar to many others in
Chinatown, but also sells a
select range of Vietnamese
canned pickles, processed fish
products, sauces, and hard-to-
find vegetables such as Chinese
chive flowers, jungle beans and
sweet turnips (vital in spring
rolls). It also sells fresh galangal

and lemongrass, plus a range
of fresh red and green chillies.
Downstairs, you'll find
steamers and woks.

Covent Garden

APOSTROPHE

215 Strand, London WC2R
1AY
Tel: 020 7427 9890

Main shop and branches: see
Oxford Street, page 43

French Bakery

★ CARLUCCIO'S

28A Neal Street,
London WC2H 9QT
Tel: 020 7240 1487
Fax: 020 7497 1361
Website: www.carluccios.com
Open: Mon-Fri 8am-8pm, Sat
10am-7pm, Sun 12pm-6pm
Closed: some Bank holidays.
Tube: Covent Garden **Bus:** 14,
19, 24, 29, 38, 176 **Payment:**
cash, cheque, Amex, Delta,
Electron, Maestro,
MasterCard, Solo, Visa
Catering, food-to-go, mail order

Italian
Delicatessen
Café

The name Carluccio is
possibly the most recognized
Italian name in London and
deservedly so, for this pretty
Italian deli in Neal Street now
has branches all over town.
Priscilla and Antonio opened
this, the first Carluccio's
Italian food shop, in 1991 in
Covent Garden, bringing the
finest regional Italian food to
London. They have since
opened a raft of 'caffés with
food shops', so that Londoners

Food Lovers' Fairs

Henrietta Green, award-winning food writer and broadcaster, has dedicated her life to the British culinary scene. For many years she has been championing simple, well-made, high-quality produce and is an ardent supporter of small, specialist food producers. She pushed for the introduction of the traditional farmers' market and is responsible for the Food Lovers' Fairs, now well established and an absolute must for dedicated food lovers and those wanting to find the best that Britain's farmers and growers have to offer. All of the producers and suppliers are personally vetted by Henrietta, who has strict criteria: suppliers should have sustainable farming practices, traceable husbandry, reliable methods and ingredients, and, above all, the food should taste superb.

The first Fair was held at St Christopher's Place in London in 1995, with just 25 stalls. The aim then was, and still is, to give the public far greater access to specialist food producers from Britain and to allow them to talk to each other directly, thereby creating an awareness of how good food is produced, plus an understanding of what people want. In 1998, Henrietta organized a Fair at Borough Market which turned out to be so successful (30,000 people visited the Fair over three days) that it has now become a regular Saturday market (page 157). Since then, the Food Lovers' Fairs have gone from strength to strength, with the Covent Garden Fair now a regular fixture for the first weekend in November. Every year, more than 120 award-winning producers from all over Britain set up their stalls in the bustling Piazza of Covent Garden, while celebrity chefs demonstrate their culinary skills, using only produce sourced from the Fair. There are also tastings and workshops and many of the local restaurants run special 'Food Lovers' Fair' menus.

For more information on Food Lovers' Fairs in London and around the country, telephone:020 8206 6111 or visit:www.foodloversbritain.com

can combine eating and shopping in an attractive, bustling environment. The Neal Street shop is a cornucopia of delicious Italian items, most of which are exclusively imported from the various regions and personally selected by Priscilla and Antonio, who are always sourcing new products. Mushrooms are Antonio's forte, and the shop therefore stocks dried mushrooms, fresh wild mushrooms in season, pastes, porcini and much sought-after fresh white truffles when available. Look out, too, for Parma ham, speck, salume, aged Parmesans, organic fruit, vegetables and herbs, duck eggs, a huge variety of pasta, extra virgin olive oils, Balsamic vinegars, sauces, rice and confectionery. There is also an excellent range of freshly baked Italian bread. Carluccio's offers a Christmas gift catalogue and a year-round mail-order service of its seasonal wares, as well as attractively wrapped foodie gift ideas, boxes and hampers.

Branches: see Chelsea, page 21, Docklands, page 160, Ealing, page 80, Hampstead, page 120, Islington, page 142, Kensington, page 92, Oxford Street, page 43, Putney, page 183, St John's Wood, page 130, Smithfield, page 66

★ MONMOUTH COFFEE COMPANY

Coffee

27 Monmouth Street, London WC2H 9EU
Tel: 020 7379 3516
Mail-order tel: 020 7645 3561
Fax: 020 7645 3565
Website: www.monmouthcoffee.co.uk
Open: Mon-Sat 8am-6pm
Closed: Sun, some Bank holidays, 25, 26 Dec., 1 Jan.
Tube: Covent Garden, Tottenham Court Road **Bus:** 14, 19, 24, 29, 38, 176 **Payment:** cash, cheque, Delta, Maestro,

---

‟Buy only what you can eat in a day or two. Cheese is always at its best when fresh cut and pieces never improve with keeping. You can no more mature a slice of cheese than you can age a glass of wine. "Little and often" is the best guide for cheese buying. ”

Patrick Rance, from *The Great British Cheese Book*

MasterCard, Visa
Catalogue, mail order, wholesale

This fantastic shop supplies many of London's restaurants – and others that are further afield – with delicious and unusual coffee. Its wares are available to the public as well: you can buy freshly roasted and ground beans to taste in the little sampling room at the back, or to drink as an espresso or cappuccino in the café. The shop offers around 10 to 12 varieties of beans, and a few basics are always available, including single estates from Costa Rica and Colombia. It also stocks two or three certified organic coffee varieties. Monmouth Coffee Company's real speciality, however, is seeking out coffee with a difference. The southern Ethiopian beans, which come from a small town called Yirgacheffe, are a good example of this. The locals pick the beans from the wild – coffee is thought to have originated in this part of the world – then clean and process them in situ.

Branch: see Borough, page 156

British Cheese Shop

★ NEAL'S YARD DAIRY
17 Shorts Gardens,
London WC2H 9UP
Tel: 020 7240 5700
Mail-order tel: 020 7645 3555
Fax: 020 7240 2442
Website:
www.nealsyarddairy.co.uk
Open: Mon-Thurs 11am-

6.30pm, Fri and Sat 10am-6.30pm **Closed:** Sun, Bank holidays **Tube:** Covent Garden
Bus: 14, 19, 24, 29, 38, 176
Payment: cash, cheque, Delta, Maestro, MasterCard, Visa
Export, mail order, wholesale

This is undoubtedly one of the finest cheese shops in the country. It stocks almost exclusively British and Irish cow's, goat's and sheep's cheeses, many of which are unpasteurized. This is a passion of the owner (and driving force behind this country's cheese-making revolution), Randolph Hodgson, who also happens to be a former chairman of the Specialist Cheesemakers' Association. Neal's Yard Dairy is more than just a shop – its staff is helpful and knowledgeable and will offer you samples to taste before you buy. All of the cheeses – among them Montgomery Cheddar (possibly Britain's best), Mrs Kirkman's famous Lancashire, Double Gloucester and a host of lesser-known varieties – are handmade on farms throughout the country using traditional methods, and they are often selected and bought directly from the farms. Try Tymsboro from Sleight Farm near Bath, a pyramid-shaped ash-covered goat's cheese. The excellent Burland Green is an organic, soft-ripening cheese in the style of a Brie or Camembert. The shop also sells cream, yoghurt from Neal's Yard Creamery, butter, bread, fresh oatcakes from Staffordshire and fabulous cheese straws from & Clarke's (page 92).

Branch: see Borough, page 156

French Pâtisserie

PÂTISSERIE VALERIE
8 Russell Street,
London WC2B 5HZ
Tel: 020 7240 0064

Main shop and branches: see Soho, page 54

French Bakery Pâtisserie

PAUL
29 Bedford Street,
London WC2E 9ED
Tel: 020 7836 3304
Fax: 020 7836 5324
Website: www.paul.fr
Open: Mon-Fri 7.30am-9pm, Sat and Sun 9am-8pm **Closed:** Bank holidays **Tube:** Covent Garden **Bus:** 14, 19, 24, 29, 38, 176 **Payment:** cash, cheque, Delta, Maestro, MasterCard, Visa

This wood-panelled French bakery and pâtisserie launched in 2001, although the business was first founded in 1889. There is a wide array of bread on offer, all arranged in huge baskets on the counters. Choose from poppy seed flutes, *pain de campagne* and *pain aux noix* or try flavoured *fougasses* – varieties include olive oil, anchovy and onion. Brioches are popular with those popping in for breakfast on their way to work, while for a self-indulgent treat, the pastries are divine – *rhubarbe tartelette*, *millefeuille* or *beignets* are just some of the treats you'll find.

Branches: see Hampstead, page 121, Knightsbridge, page 35, Marylebone, page 41, Temple, page 71

Fitzrovia

★ PLANET ORGANIC
22 Torrington Place,
London WC1E 7HJ
Tel: 020 7436 1929

Wholefood Organic Food Hall

Main shop and branches: see Bayswater, page 16

★ VILLANDRY
170 Great Portland Street,
London W1W 5QB
Tel: 020 7631 3131
Fax: 020 7631 3030
Website: www.villandry.com
Open: Mon-Sat 8am-10pm, Sun 11am-4pm **Tube:** Great Portland Street **Bus:** 7, 8, 10, 25, 55, 73, 98, 135, 176, C2 **Payment:** cash, cheque, Amex, Delta, Maestro, MasterCard, Visa
Catering, food-to-go, mail order, restaurant, bar

Food Hall

This large and elegant food shop offers one of London's best, mainly French, delicatessens. At least 30% of its produce is organic and ranges from fresh venison medallions, Italian salume, French pâtés and *rillettes* (don't miss the wide range of French charcuterie), via unique lines of dairy produce (sheep's milk, sheep's milk yoghurt with chestnut purée and fromage frais), to crispbread, biscuits and confectionery of British, French and American origin. The in-house *traiteur* section has a good selection of prepared meals. You'll also find fresh organic fruit and vegetables, which are delivered weekly from a small British farm. (A buyer also visits New Covent Garden Market daily for French and Italian produce.) Non-organic ranges tend to be of sound artisanal origin and are just as desirable: look out for a good range of French, Italian and English cheeses, which are delivered weekly, and kiln-roasted salmon and cold-smoked trout that come straight from the Woodcock smokery in Cork. The tempting fresh bread and pâtisserie are largely baked on the premises; the apple *feuilletées* and frangipane fruit tarts have won wide acclaim. Prices reflect the high quality, and the stock varies, but each visit is rewarded by new discoveries.

Knightsbridge

Food Hall

★ HARRODS

Brompton Road,
London SW1X 7XL
Tel: 020 7730 1234
Fax: 020 7893 8945/7581 0470
Website: www.harrods.com
Open: Mon-Sat 10am-7pm and Sun 10am-7pm during the Jan and July sales **Closed:** Sun, Bank holidays **Tube:** Knightsbridge **Bus:** 14, 19, 22, 52, 74, 137, C1 **Payment:** cash, cheque, Amex, Delta, Euros, Harrods card, Maestro, MasterCard, Visa **Bespoke delivery, bespoke hampers and picnics, catalogue, catering, food advisory service, food-to-go, mail order**

The Food Hall covers a major part of the ground floor – nearly 24,000 square feet – of this world-famous department store. It is a stunning area, boasting vaulted ceilings, original light fittings and Doulton tiles, many of which date from the turn of the century. The displays are spectacular and colourful, particularly the wet fish display, which incorporates a new design every day. It is all a feast for the eyes, as well as for the shopping basket, with over 350 types of cheese on offer, 150 types of bread, 150 varieties of tea (many single estate garden tea), wines and spirits, charcuterie, smoked fish, pasta and exotic fruit and vegetables. Scottish beef is available, as well as venison and lamb, some of it from the chairman's Belugavan estate. You'll find treats galore, many of which can be packaged as gifts. For a snack or meal, try one of Harrods' 22 bars and restaurants.

Food Hall
Organic

★ HARVEY NICHOLS

Knightsbridge,
London SW1X 7RJ
Tel: 020 7235 5000
Fax: 020 7235 5020
Website:
www.harveynichols.com
Open: Mon-Fri 10am-8pm, Sat
10am-7pm, Sun 12pm-6pm
Tube: Knightsbridge **Bus:** 14, 19,
22, 52, 74, 137, C1 **Payment:**
cash, cheque, Amex, Diners
Club, Electron, JCB, Maestro,
MasterCard, Solo, Visa
**Christmas hamper brochure,
delivery, food-to-go, mail order,
picnic hampers**

Situated at the very top of the
building, Harvey Nichols'
Foodmarket is a mecca for
foodies. Esoteric packets and jars
of sauces and relishes, pasta,
grains and oils from every corner
of the earth are laid out on high-
tech metal display racks. Many of
the products are sold under
Harvey Nichols' own label and
are beautifully packaged. For the
lazy or novice cook, there are
'kits' for dishes such as risotto
and *pasta e fagioli*. A serious wine
shop at one end abuts a sushi bar
with a moving counter. The
perimeter of the room is lined
with bread, fish, charcuterie and
fresh meat counters, where
butchers are on hand to advise
and cut joints to order. Huge
baskets of seasonal, mainly
organic fruit and vegetables form
a colourful display, with an
impressive array of wild
mushrooms in season. Have a
coffee before you fight your way
down the escalators (or, better
still, use the express lift), or enjoy
a meal at the acclaimed Fifth
Floor Restaurant.

LA PICENA

5 Walton Street,
London SW3 2JD
Tel: 020 7584 6573
Open: Mon-Fri 9am-7pm, Sat
9am-5pm **Closed:** Sun,
Christmas, Easter holidays **Tube:**
Knightsbridge, South
Kensington **Bus:** 14, 49, 74, 345,
C1 **Payment:** cash, cheque,
Delta, Maestro, MasterCard,
Visa
Food-to-go

Italian
Delicatessen

Lina de Angelis opened this
wonderful neighbourhood deli
and *traiteur,* which is named
after her home town of Ascoli
La Picena, in 1974. With her
faithful aides, Maria and
Antonio, who have been with
her for more than 20 years, she
still does all of the buying and
runs the shop with great
pleasure and pride. The front
window display features Italian
favourites such as fresh calves'
liver, breaded veal escalopes,
chicken Kiev, veal chops, veal
roast, *osso buco* and free-range
chicken. Inside, in addition to
the usual Italian ingredients,
there are also excellent home-
made pasta sauces including
pesto, fiery arrabiatta, *vongole,*
bolognese,
walnut and
delicious
mushroom with
porcini

sauces. Seasonal fruit and vegetables are imported from Italy – look out for the small furry, vineyard peaches in mid-summer – and there is a small but high-quality range of salad ingredients including radicchio, endive and chicory. Downstairs, the fridges groan with food-to-go such as stuffed aubergines and peppers, lasagne, cannelloni, gnocchi, sausage stew, cooked chicken and a variety of salads and finger foods. Antonio prepares the meats and cooked dishes daily.

French Pâtisserie

PÂTISSERIE VALERIE
215 Brompton Road,
London SW3 2EJ
Tel: 020 7823 9971

Main shop and branches: see Soho, page 54

French Bakery

PAUL
73 Gloucester Road,
London SW7 4SS

Main shop and branches: see Covent Garden, page 32

Marylebone

Sausages

BIGGLES
66 Marylebone Lane,
London W1U 2PF
Tel: 020 7224 5937
E-mail: orders@ebiggles.co.uk
Website: www.ebiggles.co.uk
Open: Mon 10am-4.30pm, Tues-Fri 10am-6pm, Sat 10am-4.30pm **Closed:** Sun, Bank holidays **Tube:** Bond Street **Bus:** 6, 7, 10, 12, 13, 15, 23, 73, 94,
98, 113, 135, 137, 139, 159, 189
Mainline station: Marylebone
Payment: cash, cheque, Delta, Maestro, MasterCard, Visa
Delivery depending on quantity, special orders with notice

Colin Bailey makes his sausages in the basement of this small shop, which is located just minutes from bustling Oxford Street. Since 1989, he has built up a following of loyal customers, especially among ex-pat South Africans, who come for the *boerewors* – they say they're the best in town. Bailey claims to be the only sausage-maker in London not to use bread additives or MSG in his sausages, which are also gluten-free. The garlic-flavoured Toulouse sausages are extremely popular, but you'll also find traditional British bangers, as well as Greek, Hungarian, American, Italian, French and Middle Eastern varieties. Cooked sausages are available at lunchtime to take away.

CHOCCYWOCCYDOODAH
47 Harrowby Street,
London W1H 5EA
Tel/Fax: 020 7724 5465
Website:
www.choccywoccydoodah.com
Open: Wed-Fri 10am-6pm (closed 2pm-3pm), Sat 11am-6pm **Closed:** Sun-Tues **Tube:** Edgware Road, Marble Arch
Bus: 6, 7, 15, 16, 23, 36, 98
Payment: cash, cheque, debit cards
Nationwide deliveries for

Chocolate Wedding cakes

wedding cakes, catalogue

This shop, which relies on (rapidly growing) reputation rather than passing trade, is well worth a visit, if only to see the fantastic display of doric-column-based fantasy wedding cakes. You can, meanwhile, drink in the wonderful Belgian chocolate aroma, nibble on a violet rum cream and pick up a bag of truffles. (The Belgian truffles are imported, while the British-style chocolates – including rose and violet creams, Bucks fizz truffles and white chocolate-coated ginger – are home-made at Choccywoccydoodah's Brighton base.) The shop also sells sweets for children, including hollow chocolate figures. But celebration cakes are the thing, and the selection process is aided by a plush red-cushioned sofa. The 'towering Rococo tiers, baroque cherubic fantasies, decadent gothic gargoyles and rose-strewn country garden columns' are dazzling. The work of former graphic designer Christine Taylor, they're made entirely of chocolate, with ganache-layered, dense chocolate cake centres and sculptural elements formed from white and dyed chocolate.

★ DE GUSTIBUS

53 Blandford Street,
London W1U 7HL
Tel/Fax: 020 7486 6608
Website: www.degustibus.co.uk
Open: Mon-Fri 7am-4.30pm
Closed: Sat, Sun, Bank holidays
Tube: Baker Street **Bus:** 2, 13, 30, 74, 82, 113, 139, 189, 274
Payment: cash, cheque
Food-to-go

Dan Schickentanz is a name to reckon with in the world of bread. Passionate about sourdough, he has progressed to supplying some of the finest chefs in the country. (Raymond Blanc was one of the first.) You can still enjoy Schickentanz's bread, which is baked in Abingdon, Oxfordshire, at markets (see Borough Market, page 156), various food fairs – and here, of course. Choose from a wide selection, which includes bagels and six-day

Bakery
Organic

DIVERTIMENTI

33-34 Marylebone High Street, W1U 4PT
Tel: 020 7935 0689
Website: www.divertimenti.co.uk

In the Area This, Divertimenti's flagship store, is the ultimate cookware shop and is so big you could spend hours just browsing through the cake decorating section. As well as two floors of cookware, tableware and gadgets, there is also a café that sells coffee, juices and home-made snacks. You'll find pretty much everything from pastry cutters to high-tech juicers. Demonstrations and classes with celebrity chefs are held in the cookery theatre downstairs.

Branch: 227-229 Brompton Road, London SW3 2EP **Tel:** 020 7581 8065

sourdough, cholla, Black Forest rye, Irish wheaten or linseed, roasted onion rye, Old Milwaukee rye, focaccia and date and walnut loaves. You can also enjoy sandwiches, soups, home-made vegetarian dishes, fresh juices and coffee either inside or at the few tables outside on the pavement.

Branches: see Borough, page 156, City, page 58

Fishmonger

FISHWORKS
89 Marylebone High Street, London W1U 4QW
Tel: 020 7935 9796
Mail-order tel: 0800 052 3717
Website: www.fishworks.co.uk
Open: Tues-Sat 10am-10.30pm
Closed: Sun, Mon
Tube: Baker Street **Bus:** 2, 13, 18, 27, 30, 74, 82, 113, 139, 189, 205, 274, 453 **Mainline station:** Marylebone **Payment:** cash, cheque, Amex, Delta, Diner's Card, MasterCard, Maestro, Visa
Mail order

Former accountant Mitchell Tonks launched the first FishWorks in Bath in the 1990s and now counts five of the award-winning fishmongers/restaurants/ cookery schools in his estate – with Harvey Nichols concessions and 14 more standalone sites in the pipeline. The philosophy behind the venture is to provide the highest-quality fish and seafood possible. And the fish and

Church Street Market

Open: Tues-Sat 9am-5pm **Closed**: Sun, Mon, Bank holidays **Tube:** Edgware Road **Bus:** 6, 7, 8, 15, 16, 16a, 23, 36, 98

In spite of its central London location, few people outside the area visit this good-value street market. During the week, several fruit and veg stalls congregate at the Edgware Road end, but on Fridays and Saturdays there can be over 200 stalls selling fruit, vegetables, cheap packeted and tinned foods, wholefoods such as dried pulses, fruit, nuts, plants, herbs, spankingly fresh fish and raw or cooked shellfish. You can also find general household goods and bric-à-brac. There are several specialist Asian food shops at the edges of the market.

WORTH A DETOUR

The Sea Shell, 49-51 Lisson Grove, Tel: 020 7224 9000 – best fish and chips in London

shellfish are, indeed, sparklingly fresh. FishWorks' brokers are stationed along the Cornish coast – at Newquay, Padstow, Fowey, St Mawes and Newlyn's quayside fish auction – every morning, and the fish is gracing the shops' counters the next day. You'll find line-caught mackerel, small red mullet, lemon sole, wild mussels, oysters and cockles, plus an extensive range of smoked seafood. The friendly staff will prepare all fish to your specifications and are bursting with advice on further preparation and cooking. If you can't make it to the shops in Marylebone or Chiswick, you can arrange home delivery through FishWorks' overnight courier service.

Branch: see Chiswick, page 76

Butcher
Game Dealer

★ THE GINGER PIG

8–10 Moxon Street,
London W1U 4EW
Tel: 020 7935 7788
Open: Mon–Sat 8.30am–6.30pm,
Sun 9.30am–3.30pm
Tube: Baker Street
Bus: 2, 13, 18, 27, 30, 74, 82,
113, 139, 189, 205, 274, 453
Mainline station: Marylebone
Payment: cash, cheque, Delta,
MasterCard, Maestro, Visa
Prepared meats and dishes to order

Building on the success of his stand at Borough Market, Tim Wilson launched this superb butcher's shop in 2004. Nearly everything you'll find here comes from his farm in North Yorkshire and is 100% organic and free range. Look out for expertly hung beef from Wilson's herd of Longhorn cattle; lamb and mutton from his Swaledale and Blackface sheep; great cuts of pork, sausages and dry-cured bacon from his Tamworth, Berkshire, Saddleback and Old Spot pigs; and chicken from his flock of Rhode Island Red and Dorking chickens. The shop's pies, pâtés and terrines are made – often right in front of you – by its skilled staff, giving new meaning to the phrase 'fully traceable'. It's little wonder The Ginger Pig is the butcher of choice for exclusive restaurants such as The River Café, Annabel's and George.

★ GREEN VALLEY

36 Upper Berkeley Street,
London W1H 5QF
Tel: 020 7402 7385
Fax: 020 7723 2545
Open: daily 8am-12am
Tube: Edgware Road, Marble Arch **Bus:** 6, 15, 16, 23, 36, 98
Payment: cash, Delta, Maestro, MasterCard, Visa, Solo
Catering (specialities: big parties, Christmas, Ramadan), food-to-go

Hayam Beany, the owner of this gleaming shop, is on hand at all hours, good-humouredly helping staff and customers. Her enlarged shop now includes a juice bar (choose from melon, blackberry, amarind and papaya juices – the

Middle
Eastern
Food Hall

list is endless), ice cream counter and coffee bar, which offers coffee either ground or as beans. The Middle Eastern pastries and sweets are delicious and include baklava and huge blocks of nougat. Fresh fruit and veg are at the front of the shop (deliveries come from Cyprus, Jordan and the Lebanon), and in season you'll find quince, fresh olives, purslane, rocket, Lebanese salad thyme and fresh herbs, dates, figs, watermelons, green almonds and huge sweet tomatoes from the Lebanon. Among the more unusual items are trimmed, cored courgettes (ready for stuffing), small cucumbers and purple carrots. Towards the back of the store are barrels of pickles and at least nine types of olives. Next comes fresh meat – look out for the home-made lamb sausages, which are flavoured with chillies and spices or pine nuts, and the *bastourma* (cured, dried beef fillet flavoured with herbs). At the back of the shop, you'll find a deli counter offering an array of takeaway dishes (all of which are prepared in the downstairs kitchens), including tabbouleh, *kibbeh*, vegetable salads, falafel, filled *sanbusak* pastries, real Greek Kefalotiri, Syrian and Lebanese plaited cheese and the highly flavoured *shanklish* from northern Lebanon. There are also raw lamb kebabs and kofte (all halal meat of the highest quality), dried and tinned goods, and dried limes,

Grenadine and pomegranate molasses for Iranian cooking.

INTERNATIONAL CHEESE CENTRE

Cheese Shop

5 Marylebone Station,
Melcombe Place,
London NW1 6JJ
Tel: 020 7724 1432

Main shop and branches: see City, page 58

LA BELLE BOUCHERIE

Middle Eastern Butcher Grocer

3–5 Bell Street,
London NW1 5BY
Tel: 020 7258 0230
Open: Mon-Sat 9am-9pm, Sun 11am-8pm **Tube:** Edgware Road
Bus: 6, 16, 98 **Mainline station:** Marylebone, Paddington
Payment: cash

This bustling, Algerian-owned butcher/grocer stocks a good range of foods for Middle Eastern cooking. You'll find high-quality halal meat, including spicy kofte ready for the grill, plus home-made merguez sausages. Couscous and burghul are sold loose in various grades. Also available are green tea, preserved lemons, dried apricots, Turkish delight, good-value extra virgin olive oil and pomegranate molasses for Iranian cooking. The shop also carries couscousières and tagines.

★ LA FROMAGERIE

Cheese Shop

2-4 Moxon Street
London W1U 4EW
Tel/Fax: 020 7935 0341

Bakery

Main shop: see Highbury, page 141

LE PAIN QUOTIDIEN

72–75 Marylebone High Street, London W1U 5JW
Tel: 020 7486 6154
Fax: 020 7486 6164
Website: www.lepainquotidien.com
Open: Mon-Fri 7am-9pm, Sat 8am-9pm, Sun 9am-9pm
Tube: Baker Street **Bus:** 2, 13, 18, 27, 30, 74, 82, 113, 139, 189, 205, 274, 453 **Mainline station:** Marylebone **Payment:** cash, cheque, Delta, MasterCard, Maestro, Visa
Catering

Belgian chef Alain Coumont launched the first Le Pain Quotidien in Brussels in the early 1990s, and in just over a decade it has spawned more than 45 bakeries/cafés worldwide. Even this branch, the UK's first, is set to be joined by two sites in Sloane Square and Trafalgar Square by mid-2007. Le Pain Quotidien's raison d'être is quite simply to provide 'good daily bread', according to operations manager Venetia Bladon. The excellent sourdough loaves, which are hand formed in Belgium and baked on the premises, are all prepared using sourdough leaven and organic, spelt flour. You'll also find delicious baguettes, rolls, and hazel and raisin bread, while the desserts include alluring fruit and crème brûlée

tarts, Belgian brownies, chocolate cheesecake and gorgeous full-sized or mini chocolate *bombes*. Le Pain Quotidien also sells its own range of sweet and savoury spreads – don't leave without trying the scrumptious Brunette praline. Everything can be taken away or eaten at the café's trademark long table with salads, La Fromagerie cheeses (page 141), The Ginger Pig meats (page 38) and delicious coffee served in Continental-style bowls.

ORRERY EPICERIE

55 Marylebone High Street, London W1M 3AE
Tel: 020 7616 8036
Fax: 020 7616 8080
Website: www.orrery.co.uk
Open: Mon-Fri 8am-7pm, Sat and Sun 10am-6pm **Tube:** Baker Street **Bus:** 2, 13, 18, 27, 30, 74, 82, 113, 139, 189, 205, 274, 453
Mainline station: Marylebone
Payment: cash, cheque, Amex, Delta, MasterCard, Maestro, Visa
Food-to-go, picnic hampers

Delicatessen
Traiteur

This small but perfectly formed gourmet *traiteur* is tucked beneath the Conran Group's acclaimed Orrery restaurant in a converted stable block. Unsurprisingly, its principal line is the food-to-go, which is prepared daily in Orrery's kitchen and at its Islington sister restaurant, Almeida. On our visit, the spread included glistening potato and pasta

Mr Christian's

Notting Hill – *see page 104*

Hope and Greenwood

Dulwich – *see page 162*

Golden Gate
Grocers

Chinatown – *see page 26*

Atari-Ya

Finchley – *see page 119*

salads, semi-dried tomatoes, terrine of foie gras and pâté. These dishes are supplemented by top-notch cheeses from Parisian cheesemaker Jacques Vernier, Machiavelli meats, and crusty bread and devilish desserts from Clerkenwell's Comptoir Gascon (page 61) and Blackheath's Boulangerie Jade. Elsewhere, the product range is eclectic but uniformly excellent. You'll find jars of Seggiano roasted vegetables, Accoceberry prepared meals – including the Basque specialty Axoa (minced lamb and tomatoes drenched in gravy) – from France, Iranian caviar, herbs and spices from Moroccan outfit Argania, Esprit Gourmand dried fruit and Amedei chocolates from Italy. Locals adore the friendly baristas, who start preparing their regular cups of coffee as soon as they spot them approaching.

French
Pâtisserie

PÂTISSERIE VALERIE
105 Marylebone High Street,
London W1M 3BD
Tel: 020 7935 6240

Main shop and branches: see Soho, page 54

French
Bakery
Pâtisserie

PAUL
115 Marylebone High Street,
London W1U 4SB
Tel: 020 7224 5615

Main shop and branches: see Covent Garden, page 32

★ ROCOCO
45 Marylebone High Street,
London W1U 5HG
Tel: 020 7935 7780

Main shop: see Chelsea, page 25

SPECK
6 Thayer Street,
London W1
Tel: 020 7486 4872

Main shop: see Holland Park, page 91

Mayfair

ALLENS LTD
117 Mount Street,
London W1K 3LA
Tel: 020 7499 5831
Fax: 020 7409 7112
Open: Mon-Fri 4am-3.30pm, Sat 5am-12pm **Closed:** Sun, Bank holidays **Tube:** Green Park **Bus:** 2, 8, 9, 10, 14, 16, 19, 22, 36, 38, 73, 74, 82, 137, 137a **Payment:** cash, cheque
Free local deliveries

Worn mosaic entrance tiling, deeply concave butchers' blocks and no-mod-cons payment via a sliding window at the back of the shop are just some of the signs that confirm the venerable age (some 150 years) of this well-established Mayfair butcher. Whole lamb and beef carcasses, braces of gamebirds in full plumage, plus winches and meat hooks of grand proportions fill the windows of this high-quality, traditional butchers. You can, of course,

Chocolate

Italian
Delicatessen

Butcher
Game dealer

request fillet of grass-fed, four-week-hung Scotch beef – though rib joints, with their creamy yellow fat marbling, suggest themselves more strongly. The pork and lamb have equally fine pedigree, while the range of game is unmatched, as one might expect of the supplier to The Ritz and other top London restaurants. While anything from teal to foie gras may be found here in season, you should phone through any unusual requests to assure availability.

Chocolate

CHARBONNEL ET WALKER

1 The Royal Arcade,
28 Old Bond Street, London
W1S 4BT
Tel: 020 7491 0939
Fax: 020 7495 6279
Website: www.charbonnel.co.uk
Open: Mon-Sat 10am-6pm
Closed: Sun, Bank holidays **Tube:**
Green Park **Bus:** 9, 14, 19, 22, 38
Payment: cash, cheque, Amex,
Delta, Maestro, MasterCard,
Visa
Mail order

Charbonnel et Walker has been Britain's Master Chocolatier since 1875. In that year, King Edward VII, then the Prince of Wales, encouraged Madame Charbonnel to leave a chocolate house in Paris to work alongside Mrs Walker in London. The royal connection continues today, in that the shop holds a Royal Warrant as a manufacturer of chocolates to the Queen. Luscious handmade chocolates,

from truffles to sugared almonds, can be bought in a variety of glamorous boxes that are fit for every celebratory occasion. Its drinking chocolate powder is 'England's finest'. Charbonnel et Walker now has concessions at Harrods (page 33) and Selfridges (page 43), plus a small branch at Heathrow Airport.

THE CHOCOLATE SOCIETY

Chocolate

32-34 Shepherd Market,
London W1J 7QN
Tel: 020 7495 0302

Main shop: see Belgravia,
page 18

★ H. R. HIGGINS (COFFEE-MAN) LTD

Coffee
Tea

79 Duke Street,
London W1K 5AS
Tel: 020 7629 3913,
020 7491 8819
Website: www.hrhiggins.co.uk
Open: Mon-Fri 9.30am-5.30pm,
Sat 10am-5pm **Closed:** Sun,
Bank holidays **Tube:** Bond Street
Bus: 6, 7, 10, 12, 13, 15, 23, 73,
94, 98, 113, 135, 137, 139, 159,
189 **Payment:** cash, cheque,
Amex, Delta, JCB, Maestro,
MasterCard, Visa
Mail order

If you want to know anything about tea or coffee, this is the place to visit. The Higgins family has been running this friendly business for three generations, and today it offers one of the largest selections in London – more than 40 types of coffee and

25 kinds of tea. Coffee specialities include a mocha and mysore blend ('rich and smooth with a subtle aftertaste') and Chagga from Mount Kilimanjaro ('a bright, lively flavour, very aromatic'), but the list also includes the ever-popular Jamaica Blue Mountain and decaffeinated varieties. When you buy 2.5 kg or more, the delivery is free in the UK and you can select a 100 g sample. If shopping in nearby Bond Street has tired you out, pop in for a pick-me-up cuppa in the café.

Oxford Street

French Bakery

APOSTROPHE

23 Barrett Street,
London W1U 1BF
Tel: 020 7355 1001
Fax: 020 7355 2999
Open: Mon-Fri 7.30am-8pm, Sat and Sun 9.30am-8pm **Tube:** Bond Street **Bus:** 6, 7, 10, 13, 15, 23, 73, 96, 98, 113, 137, 139, 159, 189, 390 **Payment:** cash, cheque, all debit and credit cards

This bright, modern French-style pâtisserie/boulangerie bakes and prepares all of its food on site. You'll find scrumptious quiches, croissants, savouries, pastries and organic, rye and sourdough loaves – but the real stars here are the sandwiches. There are 15 varieties, all of which are made using the shop's own bread and unusual fillings that have been devised by a team of 'celebrity

chefs'. The fresh juices, soups and coffee – which are prepared by trained baristas using manual machines – are also excellent. It's all very French: you select the items you want, pay at the till and then receive your order on a wooden tray if you're eating in, or in smart bags and boxes if you're taking it away.

Branches: see Bloomsbury, page 19, Covent Garden, page 28, Shoreditch, page 65, Temple, page 71

★ CARLUCCIO'S

St Christopher's Place,
London W1U 1AY
Tel: 020 7935 5927

8 Market Place,
London W1W 8AG
Tel: 020 7636 2228

Fenwick, New Bond Street,
London W1S 1RQ
Tel: 020 7629 0699

Main shop and branches: see Covent Garden, page 28

SELFRIDGES

400 Oxford Street, London
W1A 1AB
Tel: 020 7629 1234
Fax: 020 7495 8321
Website: www.selfridges.co.uk
Open: Mon-Wed 10am-8pm, Thurs 10am-9pm, Fri 10am-8pm, Sat 9.30am-8pm, Sun 11.30am-6pm **Closed:** 25 Dec.
Tube: Bond Street, Marble Arch
Bus: 2, 6, 7, 10, 12, 13, 15, 16A, 23, 30, 73, 74, 82, 94, 98, 113,

Italian
Delicatessen
Café

Food Hall

135, 137, 137A, 139, 159, 189, 274 **Payment:** cash, cheque, Amex, Delta, Maestro, MasterCard, Travellers cheque, Visa

Catering, delivery, food-to-go, mail order

Selfridges' extensive food hall occupies a large part of the department store's ground floor and boasts ingredients and prepared dishes from all over the world. There are several dining areas, including a Yo Sushi, and EAT, juice, oyster, salt beef and wine bars and The Gallery, a contemporary restaurant. All of the food is helpfully arranged by type, which makes it easy to find exactly what you want. The fresh fruit and vegetable section is comprehensive and stocks a range of wild mushrooms in season. There's also a deli counter with myriad salume, hams, cooked meats, mini quiches and pies. The fishmonger's counter is excellent and offers a selection of high-quality fresh fish and seafood, including conger eel, sea urchins, Welsh laver and samphire in season. The meat counter stocks prized English salt marsh lamb in season and has a good range of sausages, plus trays of *osso buco* and calf's tails. At the *traiteur*, you can find everything you need for a last-minute dinner party, from cooked lobster, smoked salmon mousse and stuffed, ready-to-grill mussels to terrines and

salads. It also has a wonderful selection of smoked fish. You'll also find counters dedicated to cheese, pasta, pâtisserie, bread, kosher food and sashimi – and the jolly, confectionery section that abuts the food hall is a favourite among central London's sweet tooths.

★ TRUC VERT

42 North Audley Street, London W1K 6ZR
Tel: 020 7491 9988
Fax: 020 7491 7717
Open: Mon-Sat 7.30am-10pm, Sun 11am-4pm **Tube:** Bond Street, Marble Arch **Bus:** 2, 6, 7, 10, 12, 13, 15, 16A, 23, 30, 73, 74, 82, 94, 98, 113, 135, 137, 137A, 139, 159, 189, 274
Payment: cash, cheque, Amex, Delta, Maestro, MasterCard, Visa

Catering, delivery, food-to-go

Named after a beach in south-west France, this cleanly designed shop is co-owned and designed by Jean-Charles Carrarini, who set up the original Villandry (page 32). Downstairs, another co-owner, Kiwi chef Russell Cameron, does the bulk of the cooking, alongside Eilidh Pitkethley, a talented baker from New Zealand. Every day, she produces an array of fresh bread and pâtisserie, including scones, meringues, Florentines and carrot, plum and yoghurt cakes. At the takeaway counter, you can buy a variety of home-made salads, baked and cured

French
Delicatessen
Bakery
Pâtisserie

hams from the UK, France and Italy, and *saucissons secs* and bresaola. Unusual items on the day we visited included cep pâté and country pâté made by Lou Camparol. Philippe Olivier supplies the cheeses. Alongside tall jars of *confit d'oie* and cooked haricots are some unusual specialities from Brittany: *rillettes de saumon, foie de lotte* (monkfish liver) and little jars of fiery *rouille* to accompany fish soups. From the Luberon, you'll find *anchoiade provençale* and *le melet* (creamed anchovy seasoned with fennel). And for the health-conscious, there's an impressive range of La Maison du Miel honeys, many of which have specific health-giving properties, plus artisan preserves and chutneys. The shop is particularly strong on natural juices made in France by Alain Milliat (try vineyard peach, wild myrtle or quince) and speciality oils including roasted peanut oil, grapeseed oil and rapeseed oil. Free-range chicken is cooked daily on the rôtisserie, and at weekends, you'll also find roast duck, quail and other poultry.

Piccadilly

Chocolate

CASEMIR CHOCOLATES

13 Piccadilly Arcade,
London SW1Y 6NH
Tel: 020 7629 8825
Fax: 020 7629 4438
Website:
www.casemirchocolates.co.uk

Open: Mon–Wed and Sat 9.30am–6.30pm, Thurs and Fri 9.30am–7pm **Tube:** Green Park, Piccadilly Circus **Bus:** 9, 14, 19, 22, 38 **Payment:** cash, cheque, Delta, MasterCard, Maestro, Visa

Mail order, gift boxes and wedding favours to order

You'd never guess it from its unassuming premises, but Casemir Chocolates supplies many of the UK's top hotels, including Claridge's, The Connaught and The Ritz. Take one bite of the chocolates, though, and it all makes sense. Casemir's velvety-smooth confections are made using only the finest raw ingredients and are free of artificial flavours, colours and preservatives. Each piece is handcrafted by a team of Belgian and French chocolatiers – most of whom are based in Belgium, though the company hopes to move its base of operations to London in 2006. There are treats here to tickle every taste bud, but the delectable whole cherries in brandy liqueur, which won the Great Taste Awards' silver award in 2003, are worth a try. The Cuvetje Golds (small, gold foil cups filled with creamy, hazelnut praline), truffles rolled in plain chocolate flakes and white ganache with Baileys Irish Cream are also outstanding. Casemir Chocolates sells its chocolates singly and in a range of gift boxes, and also does a line of ice creams, bars suitable for diabetics and novelty chocolates. Children will love the foil-wrapped frogs and ladybirds, while the footballs, golf balls and tennis sets are perfect for sports fans.

Branch: 5A Tetherdown, London N10 1ND
Tel: 020 8365 2132. Open: Sun 10am–5.30pm

Food Hall
Catering

★ FORTNUM & MASON
181 Piccadilly,
London W1A 1ER
Tel: 020 7734 8040
Website:
www.fortnumandmason.co.uk
Open: Mon-Sat 10am-6.30pm
Closed: Sun, Bank holidays Tube: Piccadilly Circus, Green Park
Bus: 9, 14, 19, 22, 38 Payment: cash, cheque, Amex, JCB, Maestro, MasterCard, Visa,
Bespoke delivery, catalogue, catering, food-to-go, mail order

Very much on the international tourist's beat, this famous store was established as a grocery in 1707 and still has a beautiful, traditional food hall. Fortnum & Mason is renowned for its luxury goods, and you'll find a wealth of exquisite gifts and foodie treats, from quail's eggs to Sevruga caviar. There are more more than 120 types of tea, a multitude of vegetables and other groceries, confectionery (try the glacé apricots and the divine *cerisettes*) and a delightful and aromatic chocolate section. There is also a huge selection of

wines, spirits and cigars. Regional British foods are particularly prominent, and the hams, smoked salmon and kippers are carefully sourced from some of the country's top producers. The cheese counter offers an unusually fine selection of seasonal British and international cheeses. Hampers can be prepared for travelling feasts, and canapés may be ordered for parties.

JAPAN CENTRE FOODSHOP
212 Piccadilly,
London W1J 9HX
Tel: 020 7434 4218
Fax: 020 7434 0313
Open: Mon-Sat 10am-7pm, Sun and Bank holidays 11am-7pm
Closed: 25 Dec. Tube: Piccadilly Circus Bus: 9, 14, 19, 22, 38
Payment: cash, cheque, Maestro, MasterCard, Visa
Catering, mail order

Japanese
Food Hall

This Japanese mini-supermarket is situated in the heart of the Japan Centre and stocks all of the groceries you'd expect to find in a food store in Japan – from fresh fish for sushi to extra-thinly sliced beef and pork for sukiyaki. The shop stocks an excellent selection of saké, plus a wide range of basics including tea, rice, miso, soy sauce and instant noodles. It also prepares nifty lunchboxes to take away.

Japanese
Confectioner

MINAMOTO KITCHOAN
44 Piccadilly,
London W1J 0DS
Tel: 020 7437 3135
Fax: 020 7437 3191
Website: www.kitchoan.com
Open: Sun-Fri 10am-7pm, Sat
10am-8pm **Tube:** Piccadilly
Circus **Bus:** 9, 14, 19, 22, 38
Payment: cash, Amex, Delta,
Maestro, MasterCard, Visa
Catering, mail order

The second best thing to visiting
this Japanese sweet shop is
poring over its catalogue, which
is packed with items of
confectionery and pâtisserie
either imported or made on the
premises. Most are
extraordinary to the Western
eye but are infinitely desirable
to Japanese sweet tooths. There
are *wagashis* made with healthy
ingredients such as red kidney
beans, glutinous and powdered
rice, sweet potatoes, sesame and
agar-agar, and allied with
natural unrefined sugar. The
speciality *tosenka* is a whole
peach coated with Japanese-
style seaweed jelly. Its stone is
replaced with a green baby

peach, so you can eat the entire
thing. Sample any of these
treats on the premises with
some green tea, or take them
away in beautiful packaging.

PÂTISSERIE VALERIE
162, Piccadilly,
London W1J 9EF
Tel: 020 7491 1717

Main shop and branches: see
Soho, page 54

French
Pâtisserie

PRESTAT
14 Princes Arcade,
London SW1Y 6DS
Tel: 020 7629 4838
Fax: 020 7399 9977
Website: www.prestat.co.uk
Open: Mon-Sat 9.30am-6pm
Closed: Sun, Bank holidays **Tube:**
Piccadilly Circus **Bus:** 9, 14, 19,
22, 38 **Payment:** cash, cheque,
Amex, Maestro, MasterCard,
Visa
**Bespoke delivery, catalogue, mail
order**

Pâtisserie
Chocolate

Established in 1902, this is one
of London's oldest and finest
chocolate shops and is an
appointed purveyor of
chocolates to HM The Queen.
Its shelves are crammed with
luscious chocolates of every
description. You'll find 30
varieties of chocolates and
truffles, plus *marrons glacés* and
authentic Turkish Delight. The
violet creams are best sellers, but
the child in you will be delighted
by the range of nostalgic
childhood sweets, which
includes sugared mice. Don't

❝ Nothing is more joyful or
exhilarating than fresh
fish simply cooked. **❞**

Rick Stein, chef

leave without trying the cocoa-dusted Napoleon III truffles, which are handmade to Prestat's own, zealously guarded recipe.

Pimlico

GASTRONOMIA ITALIA
8 Upper Tachbrook Street,
London SW1V 1SH
Tel: 020 7834 2767
Open: Mon-Fri 9am-6pm, Sat 9am-5pm **Closed:** Sun, Bank holidays **Tube:** Pimlico, Victoria **Bus:** 2, 24, 36, 185 **Payment:** cash, cheque

Mario d'Annunzio runs this busy local delicatessen and sandwich shop where you can get delicious home-made pizza at lunchtime. Boxes of *panettone* hang from the ceiling, while the deli counter is crammed with fresh cheeses, marinated olives, grilled vegetables (peppers, artichokes, aubergines), home-made pestos and plump salamis. High-quality olive oils, wines and jars, packets, tins and bottles of every imaginable Italian product grace the shelves. Sit at one of the tables outside and enjoy a cappuccino on a sunny day.

INTERNATIONAL CHEESE CENTRE
41 The Parade, Victoria Station,
London SW1V 1RJ
Tel: 020 7828 2886

Main shop and branches: see City, page 58

RIPPON CHEESE STORES
26 Upper Tachbrook Street,
London SW1V 1SW
Tel: 020 7931 0628
Fax: 020 7828 2368
Open: Mon 1pm-4pm, Tues-Sat 8.15am-5.15pm **Closed:** Sun, Bank holidays **Tube:** Pimlico, Victoria **Bus:** 2, 36, 185, 24
Payment: cash, cheque, Delta, Maestro, MasterCard, Visa
Mail order

This spotlessly clean cheese shop run by Philip and Karen Rippon is a favourite among chefs and caterers. It stocks more than 550 cheeses – about 200 of these are French, another 200 are British and the remainder come from Italy, Germany, Spain, Scandinavia, Holland and Switzerland. Be sure to try the delicious Irish semi-soft Durrus or Gubbeen.

St James's

★ PAXTON & WHITFIELD
93 Jermyn Street,
London SW1Y 6JE
Tel: 020 7930 0259
Fax: 020 7321 0621
Website:
www.paxtonandwhitfield.co.uk
Open: Mon-Sat 9.30am-6pm
Closed: Sun, Bank holidays **Tube:** Piccadilly Circus, Green Park
Bus: 3, 6, 9, 12, 13, 14, 15, 19, 22, 23, 38, 53, 88, 94, 135, 159
Payment: cash, cheque, Amex, Delta, Maestro, MasterCard, Visa
Catalogue, mail order

Previous page

The Spice Shop

Notting Hill – *see page 106*

Borough Market

– see page 157

Berwick Street Market

Open: Mon-Sat 9am-5pm **Closed:** Sun **Tube:** Piccadilly Circus **Bus:** 3, 6, 12, 13, 14, 15, 19, 23, 38, 53, 88, 94, 139, 159

Soho, the cosmopolitan area roughly bounded by Oxford Street, Tottenham Court Road, Shaftesbury Avenue and Regent Street, has long been associated with food (and sex). There has been a fruit and vegetable market here since the 1840s, and the market in Berwick Street, if no longer particularly international or exotic, still retains much of the louche flavour of old Soho, although it has diminished in scale as a result of local council demands. Now, one side of the street is crammed with fruit and vegetable stalls, which supply the area's inhabitants and workers, and the multitude of local restaurants. If the volume of trade is high, so is the volume of the stallholders advertising their wares. Prices are generally reasonable, and scoops of tomatoes, avocados or bananas can be had for as little as £1. There are also good individual fish, cheese, herb and bread stalls.

WORTH A DETOUR

✥Leon Jaeggi & Sons, 77 Shaftesbury Avenue, Tel: 020 7434 4545, high-class catering/kitchen suppliers
✥Pages, 121 Shaftesbury Avenue, Tel: 020 7565 5959, top-knotch catering/kitchen suppliers
✥Denny's, 55A Dean Street, Tel: 020 7494 2745, food service and chefs' wear

This well-established shop, in business since 1797, is one of London's landmarks and now boasts branches in Bath, Birmingham and Stratford-upon-Avon. The emphasis is, of course, on cheese, and there are some superb examples of British, Irish and French artisanal products. The selection changes with the seasons, and there are always a couple of cheeses on special offer. Other specialities include smoked salmon, hams, pies, tea, coffee, biscuits, preserves and foie gras, plus a variety of cheese-related books and accessories. Paxton & Whitfield also runs a mail-order tasting club, which offers members a selection of cheeses every month, and organizes cheese tastings in the shop.

Soho

Coffee
Tea

★ ALGERIAN COFFEE STORES

52 Old Compton Street,
London W1D 4PB
Tel: 020 7437 2480
Fax: 020 7437 5470
Open: Mon-Sat 9am-7pm
Closed: Sun, Bank holidays **Tube:**
Leicester Square, Piccadilly
Circus **Bus:** 14, 19, 22, 24, 29,
38, 94, 176 **Payment:** cash,
cheque, Amex, Delta, Maestro,
MasterCard, Visa
Catalogue, mail order, wholesale

One of the few remaining 'real'
shops in Soho, this old-
fashioned venue, which was
established in 1887, is one of
London's leading coffee and tea
retailers/wholesalers. The rich,
enticing smell of coffee filters
out on to the pavement
whenever the door opens, and
it's like an olfactory fix inside.
Friendly staff will help you

choose from the more than 120
types of coffee on offer, from
the familiar South American
and African, to organic coffee
from Papua New Guinea. Beans
come whole, roasted or ground
to specification and even coated
in chocolate. There are over
130 types of tea available as
well, including the Indian blacks
and Formosa greens to the
lesser known black China fruit-
flavoured and herbal teas. For
sweet tooths, there's a luscious
range of chocolates and other
confectionery – and for the
practical, a huge selection of
coffee-making jugs and
machines, both for domestic
and commercial use.

AMATO

14 Old Compton Street,
London W1D 4TH
Tel: 020 7734 5733
Website: www.amato.co.uk
Open: Mon-Sat 8am-10pm, Sun
10am-8pm **Tube:** Tottenham
Court Road **Bus:** 14, 19, 22, 14,
29, 38, 94, 176 **Mainline station:**
Charing Cross **Payment:** cash,
cheque, Amex, Delta, Maestro,
MasterCard, Visa
Mail order, cakes to order

Italian
French
Pâtisserie

Everything at this charming Art
Deco café/pâtisserie is made
under the watchful eye of 'chief
cake guru' Daniel Rapacioli,
and so is really fresh and of the
highest quality. The shop's
speciality is *cannoli siciliani,* a
delicate pastry made with white
wine and filled with ricotta and
chocolate, but the cakes are also

ANYTHING LEFT-HANDED

57 Brewer Street, London W1F 9UL
Tel: 020 7437 3910
Website: www.anythingleft-handed.co.uk

In the Area Amid the quirky implements
and gadgets that fill this
shop, you will find a good
selection of products designed for left-
handed cooks. The corkscrews, peelers,
grapefruit and fish knives, ladles, pastry
slicers, can-openers and kitchen scissors are
all particularly useful.

difficult to resist. Choose from the *palmiers, tartes au citron* and *tartes aux pommes* – or from healthier fare including focaccia, a quiche of the day, and a selection of salads and handmade pasta. Amato makes celebration cakes to order and will endeavour to prepare anything you wish.

Coffee

★ A. ANGELUCCI

23B Frith Street,
London W1D 4RT
Tel: 020 7437 5889
Open: Mon-Wed, Fri and Sat 9am-5pm, Thurs 9am-1pm
Closed: Sun, Bank holidays **Tube:** Tottenham Court Road, Leicester Square **Bus:** 7, 8, 10, 14, 19, 24, 29, 38, 73, 176
Mainline station: Charing Cross
Payment: cash, cheque
Mail order

This Soho institution has changed little, if at all, since it was refurbished in the 1950s. As you walk inside, there is the wonderful, all pervasive smell of freshly ground coffee. A huge set of scales, which the shop assistants will use to weigh your beans (as they did when President de Gaulle visited the shop during wartime), sits on the shelves, and a red, enamelled grinder noisily grinds the coffee to your specifications. You can choose from 36 different types of coffee. Try Angelucci's own blend, Mokital, a medium dark roast blend used by the famous Bar Italia.

ARIGATO

48-50 Brewer Street,
London W1F 9TG
Tel: 020 7287 1722
Fax: 020 7287 7597
Open: Mon-Sat 10am-9pm, Sun 11am-8pm **Closed:** 25, 26 Dec., 1 Jan. **Tube:** Piccadilly Circus
Bus: 3, 6, 12, 13, 14, 15, 19, 22, 23, 38, 53, 88, 94, 139 **Payment:** cash, cheque, Delta, Maestro, MasterCard, Visa
Catering, food-to-go

Brewer Street has become the province of the immigrant Japanese, with several Japanese supermarkets and a number of restaurants. This cramped but bright little shop has seating, where you can enjoy the home-made lunch boxes or sushi. The shelves are packed with gaudy packets and jars imported directly from Japan. These contain all of the elements for a proper Japanese meal – soy sauces, ready-made miso and soup mixes, every type of dried seaweed and noodle, and over 50 types of saké (rice wine). Arigato also sells fresh raw fish, in case you want to make your own sushi at home.

Japanese
Grocer

Italian
Delicatessen

Food Hall
Organic

Bakery
Traiteur

I. CAMISA

61 Old Compton Street,
London W1D 6HS
Tel: 020 7437 7610
Open: Mon-Fri 8.30am-6pm, Sat
8am-6pm **Closed:** Sun, Bank
holidays **Tube:** Piccadilly Circus,
Leicester Square **Bus:** 14, 19, 22,
24 , 29, 38, 94, 176 **Payment:**
cash, cheque, Delta, Maestro,
MasterCard, Visa

This tiny Italian deli has a
wonderful aroma of coffee,
cheese and spice. Its sells every
imaginable Italian speciality,
including San Daniele and wild
boar salame, pancetta, Parmesan
and other cheeses, fresh and
packaged Italian sausages,
salume, olives in bowls and tins,
marinated artichokes, olive oils,
vinegars, fresh and dried pasta,
and Italian truffles and truffle
pastes. Other specialities include
a range of fresh pasta, with
sauces to match, and *bottarga*
(salted and dried grey mullet
roe) when available.

★ FRESH & WILD

71-75 Brewer Street,
London W1F 9US
Tel: 020 7434 3179

**Main shop and
branches: see
Notting Hill,
page 97**

THE GROCER ON WARWICK

21 Warwick Street,
London W1B 5NF
Tel: 020 7437 7776
Fax: 020 7437 7778
Website: www.groceron.com
Open: Mon–Sat 8am–11pm
Closed: Sun **Tube:** Piccadilly
Circus **Bus:** 3, 6, 12, 13, 15, 23,
88, 94, 139, 159, 453 **Payment:**
cash, cheque, Delta,
MasterCard, Maestro, Visa
Mail order

Following the success of their
Notting Hill *traiteur*, The
Grocer on Elgin, Vivienne
Hayman and Ashley Sumner
relaunched their Sugar Club
restaurant in 2005 as the sleek
Grocer on Warwick. It largely
follows the format of its sister
site but, thanks to a much larger
space, also incorporates a bakery
and acclaimed Oriental fusion
restaurant headed by chef David
Selex. He and the Notting Hill
branch's chef, Frederic Flamme,
are the talents behind The
Grocer On's range of restaurant-
quality ready meals. Packed in
clear pouches and stowed in
vast, refrigerated cabinets, these
include everything from
minted broad beans
and seaweed salad
to minestrone
soup, green
chicken curry and
black cod. All of
the dishes are
handmade from
fresh, seasonal
ingredients supplied by

specialist producers – and are free of artificial preservatives, flavourings and colourings. The Grocer on Warwick has another, unsung, hero, however. From the basement, head baker Julian Sciascia sends up a cornucopia of organic, artisanal loaves – which are also used to make the deli's selection of filled sandwiches – bagels, croissants, muffins and quiches. As if these weren't enough, you'll also find Anzac biscuits and billowing pistachio meringues. *Evening Standard* food critic Fay Maschler describes Sciascia's output as 'wicked carbohydrate temptations'.

Branch: see Notting Hill, page 101

Bakery
Pâtisserie

★ KONDITOR & COOK
99 Shaftesbury Avenue,
London W1D 5DY
Tel: 020 7292 1684

Main shop and branches: see Borough, page 156

Italian
Delicatessen

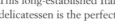

★ LINA STORES
18 Brewer Street,
London W1R 3FS
Tel: 020 7437 6482
Open: Mon-Fri 8am-6.30pm, Sat 8am-5.30pm **Closed:** Sun, Bank holidays **Tube:** Piccadilly Circus, Leicester Square **Bus:** 14, 19, 22, 38, 94 **Payment:** cash, cheque, Amex, Delta, Maestro, MasterCard, Visa

This long-established Italian delicatessen is the perfect

family-run shop, where you can get everything you need in one place. The shelves are crammed with Italianate delights including bread, packets of dried pasta, superior risotto rice, packets of polenta, tins and jars of olives, bunches of fresh basil, tomatoes, artichoke hearts, oils and vinegars. Chilled cabinets hold a variety of Italian cheeses, including buffalo mozzarella, pancetta, salami, buckets of various olives, and fresh Italian sweet and hot pork sausages. Dried porcini dangle from the ceiling along with boxes of *panettone*. Fresh pasta is made daily on the premises. The ravioli is perfect – choose from fillings such as pumpkin, sun-dried tomato and ricotta, or artichoke and truffle oil. Occasionally, the shop carries *bottarga* (salted, dried grey mullet roe), fresh porcini and black truffles.

MAISON BERTAUX
28 Greek Street,
London W1V 5DQ
Tel: 020 7437 6007
Open: Mon-Sat 8.30am-8.30pm, Sun 9.30am-8pm **Closed:** 25 Dec. **Tube:** Tottenham Court Road **Bus:** 7, 8, 10, 14, 19, 24, 25, 29, 38, 55, 73, 98, 176
Mainline station: Charing Cross
Payment: cash, cheque
Food to order

A wonderful display of pastries, savouries and some of the best croissants in town line the front window of this French

French
Pâtisserie

pâtisserie and tearoom. Founded in 1871, it has changed very little over the years. A band of regulars comes just for pastries or to while away some time in the café. Proprietor Michele Wade effortlessly creates a cosy and welcoming atmosphere. Maison Bertaux specializes in *croque en bouche* (a French wedding cake made with piles of choux buns) and is happy to prepare food to order.

French
Pâtisserie

PÂTISSERIE VALERIE
44 Old Compton Street,
London W1D 5JX
Tel: 020 7437 3466
Website:
www.patisserie-valerie.co.uk
Open: Mon-Fri 7.30am-8.30pm, Sat 8am-8pm, Sun 9am-6.30pm **Closed:** Bank holidays **Tube:** Leicester Square
Bus: 14, 19, 24, 29, 38, 176
Payment: cash, cheque, Amex, Delta, Maestro, MasterCard, Visa
Catalogue

For many, this – the original pâtisserie in a rapidly expanding chain – is still the best. Founded by Belgian Madame Valerie, it has sold cakes, tarts, eclairs and gateaux to Soho's inhabitants since 1926. Breakfast in Valerie's is a treat, thanks to the strong coffee and excellent croissants. Wedding cakes, including *croque en bouche* (an elaborate confection formed from choux buns held together

by caramelized sugar), are a speciality.

Branches: see Belgravia, page 19, Covent Garden, page 32, Kensington, page 94, Knightsbridge page 35, Marylebone page 41, Piccadilly, page 47

South Kensington

★ BAGATELLE BOUTIQUE
44 Harrington Road,
London SW7 3NB
Tel: 020 7581 1551
Fax: 020 7591 0517
Website: www.bagatelle-boutique.co.uk
Open: Mon-Sat 8am-8pm, Sun, Bank holidays 8am-6pm **Closed:** 25 Dec. **Tube:** South Kensington
Bus: 49, 70, 74
Payment: cash, cheque, Amex, Delta, Maestro, MasterCard, Visa
Catalogue, catering, delivery, food-to-go

French
Bakery
Pâtisserie

This authentic French baker supplies many restaurants with loaves made from the finest flours. (All are supplied by a mill established in 1721.) Happily, you can also buys its wares in this shop, which offers the freshest baguettes, croissants and pains au chocolat, all delivered twice daily, plus delectable pâtisserie including *bagatelle* (a vanilla bavarois and bitter chocolate mousse topped with caramelized almond biscuit). You'll also find chocolates made in Paris by a small specialist producer, charcuterie (pâtés of every possible permutation, French hams, sausages and foie gras), smoked salmon and some French cheeses. This is the place to visit for spectacular celebration cakes such as *croque en bouche* or *bûche de Noël*.

French
Delicatessen
GI Diet

THE MONTIGNAC BOUTIQUE AND CAFE

160 Old Brompton Road, London SW5 0BA
Tel/Fax: 020 7370 2010
Website: www.montignac.co.uk
Open: Mon-Fri 8.30am-9pm, Sat 8.30am-6pm, Sun 10am-5pm **Closed:** fortnight at Christmas, Bank holidays **Tube:** South Kensington, Gloucester Road **Bus:** C1 **Payment:** cash, cheque, Amex, Delta, Maestro, MasterCard, Visa
Food-to-go, mail order

This shop is French 'Eat Yourself Slim' guru Michel Montignac's English dietary centre. The idea behind the foods on offer is that all have a low glycaemic index while still being nutritionally valuable. The café/*traiteur* section offers typically French goodies such as duck confit, celeriac mash

and lentil vinaigrette, plus some surprisingly indulgent cakes and puds, and a selection of French cheeses. The own-brand Montignac products include wood-fire toasted muesli; organic pulses, pasta and grains; very French condiment-sauces including sorrell purée; superbly concentrated fruit compotes, *coulis* and preserves; biscuits and toasts; and high cocoa content chocolate. Most are suitable for diabetics. The shop's pride and joy, however, is the stoneground, organic, wood-fire-baked bread, which is flown in most days from Savoie.

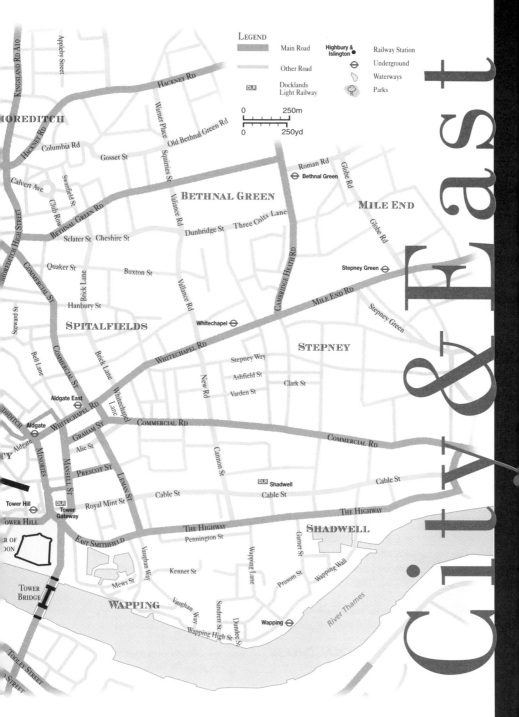

Bethnal Green Road Market

Open: Mon-Wed, Fri, Sat 8.30am-5pm, Thurs 8.30am-12.30pm
Closed: Sun, Bank holidays
Tube: Bethnal Green **Bus:** 8
Mainline station: Bethnal Green

This characterful East End street market is at the heart of the local cockney community and continues to thrive, particularly at weekends. Most of the stalls offer traditional and reasonably priced fruit and vegetables, but you can also buy Afro-Caribbean foods, cut-price foods, household goods and clothes.

City

Bakery
Organic

★ **DE GUSTIBUS**
53 Carter Lane,
London EC4V 5AE
Tel: 020 7236 0062

Main shop and branch: see Marylebone, page 36

Cheese
Shop

INTERNATIONAL CHEESE CENTRE
Liverpool Street Station,
London EC2M 7PY

Tel: 020 7628 2343
Open: Mon-Wed 7.15am-8pm,
Thurs and Fri 7.15am-8.30pm,
Sat 10.30am-7.30pm **Closed:**
Sun, Bank holidays **Tube:**
Liverpool Street **Bus:** 11, 23, 42,
100, 133, 141, 172, 214, 271
Mainline station: Liverpool
Street **Payment:** cash, cheque,
Amex, Delta, Maestro,
MasterCard, Visa
Bespoke delivery, international mail order (international), orders taken, hampers

The International Cheese Centre has a presence at four mainline stations, a clever move that has ensured its survival. The Liverpool Street shop is packed with fine groceries and a huge selection of cheeses (the list features some 400), plus honeys from round the world. The atmosphere is unintimidating and tasting is positively encouraged. While it is possible to buy a small wedge of cheese for lunch – or, indeed, a sandwich generously filled with a range of cheeses and meats – where the shop scores well is as a last-minute dinner-party stop. You'll find savoury nibbles, crisps, breadsticks, oils, dressings, pickles and chutneys aplenty. Pick up a vintage port, or you could round off your evening with a Delamain cognac or an 1893 Armagnac.

Branches: Marylebone, page 39, Pimlico, page 48, Temple, page 71

★ H.S. LINWOOD & SONS

6 Grand Avenue,
Leadenhall Market,
London EC3V 1LR
Tel: 020 7929 0554
Open: Mon-Fri 6am-3.30pm
Closed: Sat, Sun, Bank holidays
Tube: Monument, Bank **Bus:** 8,
25, 26, 35, 47, 48, 149, 242
Mainline station: Fenchurch
Street **Payment:** cash, cheque,
Amex, Diners Club, Maestro,
MasterCard, Visa
**Delivery to central London and
West End, orders taken**

This venerable fishmonger of
over a hundred years' standing
holds a Royal Warrant to HM
The Queen, though the quality
of the produce speaks for itself.
Smoked salmon is a mainstay
and various grades – 'quality
assured', 'best' and 'trimmings'
– are on offer. You'll also find
superb fresh fish including tuna,
swordfish, lobster, crab, fresh
scallops ranging from tiny
queenies to huge, succulent
'jumbos', every type of prawn
you could imagine and other
hard-to-come-by items such as
salt cod and sachets of squid
ink. A cooked seafood stand
offers the likes of cured herring,
shelled whelks, cockles, mussels,
crayfish tails and jellied eels.
There are also tins of crab and
lobster soup, fish stock and
gull's eggs. The listed building's
maroon and gold décor is a
pleasure in itself.

MAXWELL & KENNEDY

Liverpool Street Station,
London EC2M 7PN
Tel: 020 7638 2847
Open: Mon-Fri 8am-8pm, Sat
10am-6pm, **Closed:** Sun, Bank
holidays **Tube:** Liverpool Street
Bus: 11, 23, 42, 100, 133, 141,
172, 214, 271 **Mainline station:**
Liverpool Street **Payment:** cash,
cheque, Amex, Delta, Maestro,
MasterCard, Visa
**Bespoke deliveries within central
London, mail order**

This chocolate shop in the busy
Liverpool Street Station
shopping mall is designed to
catch commuters looking for
gifts and treats and, judging by
the constant buzz, it seems to
be succeeding. The formula is
one of classy, but
unintimidating background
(dark wood and gold lettering,
but cheerfully coloured boxes
and tinsel, and giggly young
staff). The young company is
Scottish in origin, but the
sweets and chocolates have a
distinctly English feel: there are
violet and rose creams, Turkish
delight, Cumbrian butter fudge,
silver and gold dragées, and
jelly fruit. A good many truffles
are pastel shaded and boldly
flavoured with strawberry,
vodka, Baileys or Malibu.
Children's novelty animals are
legion, and diabetics are catered
for, too, with a no-sugar range,
so you can be assured of finding
an appropriate gift at a
moment's notice. Since the
company linkup, chocolates are

now primarily manufactured by Charbonnel et Walker (page 42), but recipes remain true to the Maxwell & Kennedy originals.

Branch: see Docklands, page 160

Butcher
Sausages

PORTERFORD
72 Watling Street,
London EC4 9BJ
Tel: 020 7248 1396
Fax: 020 7236 5517
Open: Mon-Thurs 6.30am-6.30pm, Fri 6am-7.30pm **Closed:** Sat, Sun, Bank holidays **Tube:** Mansion House **Bus:** 8, 11, 15, 17, 23, 25, 26, 172, 242, 521
Mainline station: Cannon Street
Payment: cash, cheque, Delta, Electron, Maestro, MasterCard, Visa
Local deliveries

This excellent butcher boasts long opening hours; swift, friendly and helpful service; and a large range of impressive cuts and preparations from well-sourced meat and poultry. The latter include boned, rolled and stuffed chicken, capon and duck, with fillings such as herb, stilton, spring onion and tomato. Options for 'easy meals' include fresh chicken kiev, breaded veal escalopes and the very popular chicken royal. The shop has some really great bargains including guinea fowl and pheasant legs at ridiculously low prices, thanks to a thriving restaurant trade in supremes. You'll also find a good range of exotics

(springbok, kudur) and game in season – but purists will go for the free-range and organic Black Mountain Foods' Welsh lamb, or magnificent ribs of Scotch beef from Mathers Aberdeen Angus. Be sure to try some of the 22 varieties of home-made sausage on offer.

Clerkenwell

Spanish
Delicatessen

★ BRINDISA
32 Exmouth Market,
London EC1R 3QE
Tel: 020 7713 1666
Website: www.brindisa.com
Open: Mon-Sat 10am-6pm
Closed: Sun, Bank holidays
Tube: Angel, Farringdon
Bus: 19, 38, 63
Mainline station: Farringdon
Payment: cash, cheque, Delta, Maestro, MasterCard, Visa

Brindisa is a major wholesaler of Spanish produce and is also at Borough Market on Thursdays, Fridays and Saturdays. This branch is adjacent to the famous Moro restaurant and offers an excellent range of Spanish hams, including a Pata Negra Iberica ham that hangs from the ceiling. On our visit, we spotted chorizo from Rioja and Pamplona, and a *salchichon* made from acorn-fed pigs. The tubs of olives included the usual Spanish varieties, such as anchovy-stuffed olives, as well as the more interesting *arbequina*, which make a delicious olive oil. Other goodies typically include capers in salt, *guidillas* (pickled garlic), superior canned tuna from Ortiz, jars of aioli from Catalunya, saffron, smoked paprika, whole *piquillo* peppers from Navarra, vinegar from Jerez and unusual olive oils, such as the Nuñez de Prado. The cheeses include *Idjazabal* from the Basque country and a highly recommended sheep's cheese from Extremadura.

Branch: see Borough, page 156

French Delicatessen

★ **COMPTOIR GASCON**
63 Charterhouse Street,
London EC1M 6HJ
Tel: 020 7608 0851
Fax: 020 7608 0871
Open: Mon-Fri 8am-8pm, Sat 9am-6pm **Closed:** Sun, Bank holidays **Tube:** Farringdon
Mainline station: Farringdon
Bus: 19, 38, 63, 171a **Payment:** cash, cheque, Amex, Delta, Maestro, Mastercard, Visa

This beautiful, light and airy shop, the latest effort from Pascal Aussignac and Vincent Lebeyrie of Club Gascon fame, specializes in food and wine from south-west France. Most of the food is brought in directly from France each week, with in-house chefs preparing the cooked dishes, pâtisserie and bread on the premises. The French staff is knowledgeable and helpful – and the food counters are crammed with charcuterie including pâtés, foie gras with Sauternes, smoked

magret of duck, duck confit, Toulouse sausages and *jambon fermier*. Fish and seafood, including some wonderful smoked eel, are also on offer, alongside prepared dishes such as a delicious *civet* of wild mushrooms. Cheeses include *Ossau Iraty* from the Basque country, fresh goat's cheese and *Perail de Brebis* sheep's cheese. The bread lines – all made in the French way (*au levain*) – include rye bread, campagne and sourdough. You'll also find crystallized violet petals, walnuts in praline, prunes in Armagnac, Balsamic vinegar with figs and Le Gascon coffee. The excellent range of wine, most of which comes from south-west France, is supplemented by a small selection of champagne and some interesting aperitifs, such as the Lillet Rouge vermouth.

FLÂNEUR FOOD HALL
41 Farringdon Road,
London EC1 M 3JB
Tel: 020 7404 4422
Fax: 020 7831 4532
E-mail: mail@flaneur.com
Website: www.flaneur.com
Open: Mon-Fri 8am-10pm, Sat and Bank holidays 9am-10pm, Sun 9am-6pm **Closed:** 25, 26 Dec., 1 Jan. **Tube:** Farringdon, Chancery Lane **Bus:** 19, 38, 63, 171a **Mainline station:** Farringdon **Payment:** cash, cheque, Amex, Delta, Maestro, MasterCard, Visa
Food-to-go, local delivery, mail order, orders taken

Food Hall

Every wall in this stunning food emporium is lined with packets, bottles and jars. Many of the goods are made by small, artisanal producers using traditional methods. Provenance is important to the people running Flâneur, and they take the time to get to know their suppliers. The stock is wide-ranging and includes English, Irish, French, Italian and Spanish products, as well as items from the US and Canada and more recently introduced products from Japan and Thailand. You can pick up Gragnano pasta from Italy, Arroz Calasparra rice for paella, buckwheat noodles, fresh coffee and herbal tea, wild cranberry jam, Ortiz canned fish and aubergine dip from the Peloponnese. The deli counter offers a good selection of French cheeses – including some from Neal's Yard Dairy (page 31) – Spanish manchegos, chorizo, Salame Classico, Parma ham and *rillettes de porc*. The *traiteur* section has delicious prepared meals including tabbouleh, frittata, roasted Mediterranean vegetables and roast belly of pork. The wines are mainly French, but you'll also find a few Italian and New World varieties.

Italian
Delicatessen

★ G. GAZZANO & SONS
167-169 Farringdon Road,
London EC1R 3AL
Tel: 020 7837 1586
Open: Mon, Sat 8am-5pm, Tues, Fri 8am-6pm, Wed-Thurs 8am-5.30pm, Sun 10am-2pm **Closed:** Bank holidays **Tube:** Farringdon **Bus:** 19, 38, 63, 171a **Mainline station:** Farringdon **Payment:** cash, cheque, Delta, Maestro, MasterCard, Visa **Orders taken**

This family-run Italian deli has a devoted clientele covering the length and breadth of London. Christmas and Easter are good times to visit, as the Gazzanos' passion for sweetmeats is given full rein. *Colomba* and *panettone* come in many shapes and flavours, and include the excellent Tre Marie range. You'll also find *tartufatas*, nougats, *cavallucci*, *ricciardi* and *amaretti* in more guises than elsewhere, as well as fruit bottled in Moscato or Freisa. The range of fresh sausages and salume is impressive: you'll find Genovese, Napolitana, Lucanica, Finocchiona, wine-marinated Dolce di Carnia and the like, with *porchetta*, speck, *rostino* and *soppressata* among the other pork products. Both fresh and dried pasta are here aplenty – there are 110 shapes at the last count. Visit in the spring to secure seeds for unusual herbs and vegetables including *treviso*, long red peppers and a multitude of basils. Service is both helpful and friendly, and the shop is a past winner of the *Evening Standard*'s Best Deli of the Year award.

All the world loves a sausage. There is something of a renaissance for such hearty fare, with butchers expanding into herb, garlic and spicy types, supermarkets on the lookout for old-fashioned butchers' recipes and grocers stocking spicy Spanish chorizo and garlicky French Toulouse.

Nigel Slater

Delicatessen

MYDDELTONS
25A Lloyd Baker Street,
London WC1X 9AT
Tel: 020 7278 9192
Fax: 020 7833 8858
Open: Mon-Fri 7am-7pm, Sat
7am-6pm **Closed:** Sun, Bank
holidays **Tube:** Farringdon,
Angel **Bus:** 19, 30, 38, 63, 73,
171a **Mainline station:**
Farringdon **Payment:** cash,
cheque, Delta, Maestro,
MasterCard, Visa
Takes orders

Valued as much for its long
opening hours as for its range of
good-quality food and wine,
this neighbourhood deli stocks
a bit of everything: fruit and
veg; free-range sausages,
chickens and eggs; a selection of
40 cheeses, including the very
popular English Farmhouse
Cheddar; bread from & Clarke's
(page 92); cakes by Nadell
Pâtisserie (page 144);
Crumpton's fruit cakes;
handmade Belgian chocolates;

and Café de Paris coffee,
ground to order. Staples include
preserves from Cottage Delight,
organic jams by the All Natural
Preserving Company and fancy
pasta such as frilly *tacconi*.
Lunchtime sees a busy trade in
gourmet sandwiches.

Branch: Pâtisserie Max,
61 Amwell Street,
London EC1R 1UR
Tel: 020 7278 6181

SIMPLY SAUSAGES
341 London Central Markets,
London EC1A 9NH
Tel/Fax: 020 7329 3227
Open: Mon-Fri 8am-6pm
Closed: Sat, Sun, Bank holidays
Tube: Farringdon **Bus:** 55, 243,
505 **Mainline station:** Farringdon
Payment: cash, cheque, Delta,
Maestro, MasterCard, Visa

You will find an overwhelming
range of sausages, including
vegetarian and seasonal
varieties, in this shop. All of the

Sausages

sausages are handmade to traditional recipes, encased in natural skins and have a high meat content – but absolutely no artificial additives. Favourites include the beef and Guiness, Cheddar and spinach, mushroom and tarragon, and duck and orange varieties.

Italian Delicatessen

L. TERRONI & SONS
138-140 Clerkenwell Road, London EC1R 5DL
Tel: 020 7837 1712
Fax: 020 7837 1721
Open: Tues-Fri 9am-5.45pm, Sat 9am-3pm, Sun 9.30am-1.45pm
Closed: Mon, Bank holidays
Tube: Farringdon, Chancery Lane **Bus:** 55, 243, 505 **Mainline station:** Farringdon **Payment:** cash, cheque, MasterCard, Maestro, Visa

Established in 1878, this spacious, good-value Italian delicatessen supplies everything any true-born Italian, or Italophile, could want. Its strength lies with an abundance of staples, including four types of '00' flours; row upon row of pasta from Molisana; a vast range of Beretta salume; perhaps every style in the ubiquitous Mulino Branco, Grisbi and Loacker biscuit ranges; and more types of *savoiardi* than one imagined existed. The fresh foods include home-made pasta, sauces and *salsiccie*. You'll also find salt cod, perfect pink garlic in season, salted capers and basic fruit and veg. L. Terroni & Sons

boasts an extensive wine selection – Tignanello, Sassicaia and the best of Jermann, Maculan and Lungarotti, to name but a few – all of which are labelled with bouquet and flavour profiles. Christmas sees the shop transformed with a floor-to-ceiling stack of *panettoni* and elegant hampers.

Shadwell

HUSSEY'S
54/64 Wapping Lane, London E1W 2RL
Tel: 020 7488 3686
Open: Mon-Fri 7am-6pm, Sat 7am-5pm **Closed:** Sun, Bank holidays **Tube:** Wapping **Bus:** 100 **Mainline station:** Shadwell DLR **Payment:** cash, cheque, Delta, Maestro, MasterCard, Visa
Bespoke deliveries locally

Butcher
Game dealer
Greengrocer

Tucked among a clutch of shops is this gem of a butcher, which has been run by the Hussey family for more than 50 years. Ian Hussey takes great pride in the longevity of his business and its ability to provide a service that far exceeds what any supermarket can offer. At number 54, you'll find an extensive fruit and veg section – the quality and range of which matches any central London concern. There are also cooked meats, including ham, salt beef and roast turkey; pies; eggs ('our eggs really are free-range' a notice insists); and a selection of cheeses. At number 64, free-

Spitalfields Market *– see page 69*

Previous page Borough Market *– see page 157*

Luigi's

Chelsea – *see page 24*

Overleaf

Portobello Road Market

Notting Hill – *see page 100*

range pigs' feet, tails, and just about every bit 'except the oink' are in evidence. You'll also find carefully butchered Scotch beef and lamb – Hussey's are associate members of the Guild of Scotch Quality Meat – half a dozen varieties of home-produced sausage and black puddings from MacSweens, and game in season.

Shoreditch

French
Bakery

APOSTROPHE

42 Great Eastern Street,
London EC2A 3EP
Tel: 020 7739 8412

Main shop and branches: see
Oxford Street, page 43

Food Hall

FOOD HALL

374–378A Old Street,
London EC1V 9LT
Tel: 020 7729 6005
Open: Mon–Fri 9am–7pm, Sat and Sun 10am–5pm
Tube: Old Street
Bus: 43, 55, 76, 141, 205, 214, 243, 271
Mainline station: Old Street
Payment: cash, Delta, Maestro, MasterCard, Visa
Catering, food-to-go

Former money broker Denise Marchent and chef Malcolm Gee opened this culinary treasure trove in 2004 and are poised to launch two more branches in Barbican and Bermondsey. The Old Street site, a former dairy complete with Victorian coving and tiles,

is packed with artisanal foods. 'We're members of the Slow Food movement, so we try to use small producers,' says Marchent. Stock changes with the seasons and is mostly organic. Baker & Spice (page 20), Born & Bread, Breads Etcetera, Exeter Street Bakery and & Clarke's (page 92) deliver crusty loaves each day. The cheeses are from Neal's Yard Dairy (page 31), the coffee from Monmouth Coffee Company (page 30) and the own-label meats are supplemented by sausages, bacon and cured meats from Brindisa (page 60), The Ginger Pig (page 38), Wootton Organic and Bleiker's Family Smokehouse. You'll also find organic fruit and vegetables; Seasoned Pioneers' dried herbs and spices (page 201); a plethora of jams, relishes, chutneys and olive oils; chocolates from Prestat (page 47) and L'Artisan du Chocolat (page 18); plus a good range of mid-priced wines. Take a break from the sensory onslaught at the café, which serves weekday lunches and popular weekend brunches.

★ FRESH & WILD

196 Old Street,
London EC1V 9FR
Tel: 020 7250 1708

Main shop and branches: see
Notting Hill, page 97

Organic
Food Hall

Smithfield

★ BUTCHER & EDMONDS

Smithfield Meat Market,
London EC1A 9LH
Tel: 020 7329 7388
Fax: 020 7623 5946
Open: Mon-Fri 5.30am-4pm
Closed: Sat, Sun, Bank holidays
Tube: Farringdon, Chancery
Lane **Bus:** 17, 45, 46, 63, 243
Street **Payment:** cash, cheque,
Amex, Delta, JCB, Maestro,
MasterCard, Visa
**Delivery by arrangement, orders
taken**

Butcher & Edmonds is one of
the few original shops in the
Arcade and is regularly sought
out by media and film-makers
keen to capture the olde worlde
delights of its sawdust-coated
terracotta tiles, and cream and
maroon-washed stone walls. The
three-week hung Scotch beef is
much in demand by City Livery
companies and in directors'
dining rooms, though game in
season is its top seller. Christmas
brings bronze turkeys from
Huntingdon, while eggs come
'direct from a chap in
Woolwich'; trusted suppliers are
a mainstay of the business.
Arrive early.

★ CARLUCCIO'S

12 West Smithfield,
London EC1A 9JR
Tel: 020 7329 5904

Main shop and branches: see
Covent Garden, page 28

MEAT CITY

507 Central Markets, Farringdon
Road, London EC1A 9NL
Tel: 020 7253 9606
Website: www.meatcity.ltd.uk
Open: Mon-Fri 8.30am-6.30pm
Closed: Sat (open for collection
by arrangement), Sun **Tube:**
Farringdon, Chancery Lane **Bus:**
17, 45, 46, 63, 243 **Payment:**
cash, cheque, Delta, Maestro,
MasterCard, Visa
Orders taken, bespoke delivery

Owner Nigel Armstrong,
specializes in the finest naturally
reared, free-range meat and
poultry, all offered at competitive
prices. He has eschewed joining
the Q Guild to avoid the extra
costs involved and does not deal
in organic meat for the same
reason. After more than 20 years
in the trade, Armstrong is
confident that the meat he sells is
truly top notch. Customers come
here for three-to-four-week hung
Aberdeen Angus beef, two-week
matured free-range pork, Group-
grown veal, Royal Park venison
and Golden Promise turkey.
Frozen game and exotic meats,
including ostrich, kangaroo and
bison, are also available year
round. It's always best to pre-
order anything you require and
phone before dropping in,
however. Nigel runs a one-man
show and spends some mornings
on delivery rounds. Indeed, there
is often no meat on display,
because the business relies on
its reputation rather than on
passing trade.

" The things I look forward to with extreme passion are the first broad beans and the first peas.

Sir Terence Conran

Spitalfields

Jewish Bakery

BEIGEL BAKE
159 Brick Lane,
London E1 6SB
Tel: 020 7729 0616
Open: 24 hours, 7 days a week
Tube: Old Street **Bus:** 8, 67
Mainline station: Shoreditch
Payment: cash, cheque
Takes orders for collection

This popular beigel shop has become something of an institution, particularly in the early hours of Saturday and Sunday mornings, when it is frequented by crowds of hungry clubbers. Given its location – it's tucked right at the north end of East London's Brick Lane – a visit is something of a pilgrimage. Danny La Rue and Rod Stewart have been spotted by the amused proprietor, sending their drivers in to brave the milling munchers. You certainly don't need pop star salaries to indulge in a beigel, however: a smoked salmon and cream cheese classic costs £1.30, while a perfect, plain buttered beigel will set you back just 20p. Favourite fillings include mozzarella and cream cheese, and salt beef. You can choose to have a platzel (no hole) instead, or indulge in gigantic cream eclairs, muffins or Eccles cakes washed down with spoon-supporting tea at the zinc bar. You can even buy your daily bloomer, chollah or black bread (weekends only) here, but it's those 8,000 beigels a day that keep the place buzzing.

British Grocer

★ A. GOLD
42 Brushfield Street,
London E1 6AG
Tel: 020 7247 2487
Website: www.agold.co.uk
Open: Mon–Fri 11am–8pm,
Sun 11am–6pm
Closed: Sat **Tube:** Liverpool
Street **Bus:** 8, 11, 23, 26, 35, 42,
47, 48, 78, 100, 133, 149, 153,
205, 214, 242, 271, 344, 388
Mainline station: Liverpool
Street **Payment:** cash, cheque,
Amex, Delta, Maestro,
MasterCard, Visa
Mail order

Local residents, city workers and tourists flock to this gem of a shop, which opened in a restored Georgian townhouse in 2000. Weary of listening to criticism of British food, owners Ian and Safia Thomas have sourced some of the UK's finest products – even if that's sometimes meant coaxing suppliers out of retirement. 'We try to be a useful local shop,' says Safia. To that end, they stock Welsh eggs, artisanal cheeses from Neal's Yard Dairy (page 31), De Gustibus bread (page 36), and bacon and sausages from Cumbria's Sillfield Farm in their tiny deli area. The front of the shop is given over to the stuff of childhood memories. Handmade Welsh, Eccles and Banbury cakes and glass jarfuls of sweeties – including sugar mice with tails and crumbly fudge from Yorkshire – batter your resolve from the moment you walk in. Tucked in the back are such British treasures as sloe gin, dandelion and burdock cordial, and mead. Still excited about each new discovery, Ian enthused on our visit about the honeycombs delivered straight from the producer's London Bridge rooftop. 'Honey produced in your area keeps allergies at bay,' he says. But if that doesn't work, there are always bottles of the rare Scottish fermented whey drink, Blaand, to cure whatever ails you.

ST JOHN BREAD & WINE

Bakery

94–96 Commercial Street,
London E1 6LZ
Tel: 020 7247 8724
Fax: 020 7247 8924
Website:
www.stjohnbreadandwine.com
Open: Mon-Fri 9am-11pm, Sat 10am-11pm, Sun 10am-6pm
Tube: Liverpool Street **Bus:** 8, 11, 23, 26, 35, 42, 47, 48, 67, 78, 100, 133, 149, 153, 205, 214, 242, 271, 344, 388 **Mainline station:** Liverpool Street
Payment: cash, cheque, Amex, Delta, Maestro, MasterCard, Visa

This laid-back offshoot of Clerkenwell's St John Bar and Restaurant now houses the bakery that supplies both restaurants, as well as upmarket London eateries Anchor & Hope and Throgmortons. Each day, head baker Justin Gellatly prepares a limited selection of bread that aims, he says, to let the natural flavours shine through. The generous, crusty loaves – white, brown, sourdough, soda, raisin, and date and walnut, to name a few – are prepared with organic flour sourced from Shaftesbury's Cann Mill. There are desserts here, too, including rich, nutty brownies and the justly popular Eccles cake. But Sunday, when Gellatly prepares a batch of delicious custard-, jam- and lemon curd-filled doughnuts, is the real draw for sweet tooths. Go early to avoid disappointment.

Spitalfields Organic Market

Commercial Street
Open: Sun 10am-3pm **Tube:** Liverpool Street
Bus: 8, 26, 35, 43, 47, 48, 67, 78, 149, 242

The huge Victorian building, which takes its name from the hospital fields that once occupied this site, was once home to one of London's largest fruit and vegetable markets. A general market still operates from Monday to Friday, but in a fairly desultory way. It is at the weekend that the building really comes to life, and particularly on a Sunday, when the organic food market is held. There are stalls selling organic fruit, vegetables, juices, bread, jams, relishes, pickles and eggs. Handmade, hand-woven, hand-dyed and hand-painted are the buzz-words at other stalls in the market, some of which offer extremely attractive products. One of the other good reasons to come here is for the refreshments – if you're hungry, stalls and small restaurants around the edge of the building sell a variety of international foods such as crêpes, falafel, satays and Thai noodles.

Indian
Food Hall
Halal

TAJ STORES
112-114A Brick Lane,
London E1 6RL
Tel: 020 7377 0061/7247 3844
Fax: 020 7377 6787
Email: info@tajstores.co.uk
Website: www.tajstores.co.uk
Open: Mon-Sun 9am-9pm **Tube:** Liverpool Street, Aldgate East
Bus: 67 **Mainline station:** Shoreditch, Liverpool Street
Payment: cash, cheque, Delta, Maestro, MasterCard, Visa

The elegant red and gold frontage, with a somewhat discordant display of Coke tins, opens up to reveal a vast Bangladeshi/Indian cash-and-carry-style store that also caters amply for personal customers. Thus, you can stagger away with a well-priced 20kg box of basic rice or purchase a small packet of Watan super kernel basmati. Ghee, too, comes in small or gigantic tins, and the shop is certainly one of the best sources of bargain-priced packs of spices, both whole and ground. A fast turnover of dry goods – including spices, nuts, grains and flours – ensures freshness. The selection of Oriental foods includes Thai noodles and rice, lemongrass, lime leaf and galangal. The meats are halal, and the imported Indian ocean fish is frozen whole, in 400g/800g blocks, or as steaks of huge dimensions – but always at remarkably low prices. Otherwise, goods run the gamut from basic cookery implements – such as plastic spoons and pots and pans – to rainbow-coloured, sugar-coated fennel seed and basil seed-flavoured soft drinks.

Grocer

VERDE'S

40 Brushfield Street,
London E1 6AG
Tel: 020 7247 1924
Open: Mon–Fri 8am–8pm, Sat and Sun 11am–5pm **Tube:** Liverpool Street **Bus:** 8, 11, 23, 26, 35, 42, 47, 48, 78, 100, 133, 149, 153, 205, 214, 242, 271, 344, 388 **Mainline station:** Liverpool Street **Payment:** cash, cheque, Delta, Maestro, MasterCard, Visa
Catering, food-to-go

This Spitalfields grocer is clearly a labour of love for owners Harvey Cabaniss and Tim Whittaker. Cabaniss, formerly head chef of caterer The Urban Kitchen, has drawn on his contacts in that industry to fill the shop with the best possible products. And Whittaker, author of *The Well-Worn Interior*, has more than matched him with the shop's mix of Georgian antiques, many of which are for

sale. Pierre Marcolini chocolates, then, are encased in an antique glass cabinet, and the organic herbs are potted in lovely old containers. There's even an antique desk near the door, where Pineider stationery is displayed. (A nod, perhaps, to landlady Jeanette Winterson?) There's a strong Italian bent to the foods: the shelves groan with olive oils, polenta, breadsticks and biscotti; and the coffee, pasta, cheeses and charcuterie are all supplied by Machiavelli. But you'll also find organic fruit and

STEPPING STONES FARM SHOP

Stepping Stones Farm,
Stepney Way, London E1 3DG
Tel: 020 7790 8204

In the Area The shop at Stepping Stones Farm is just a small part of this community enterprise. The animals here are immensely child-friendly, with some rather attractive breeds on display. That said, the farm shop has won a number of prizes for its considerable range of seasonal, home-made jams, curds, jellies and marmalades – its wild plum jam, which is made from on-site plum trees, is a favourite. Its adventurous range of pickles and chutneys, which includes Kashmiri garlic with lime and coconut, and sweet-pickled green tomato, is also excellent. The pullet, bantam and duck eggs are free-range and very fresh, and the staff is happy to put together little baskets of produce.

vegetables, Rinkoff bread, Sally Clarke desserts and beautifully packaged bags of dried fruit, herbs and spices. Don't leave on weekdays without trying the superb coffee and sandwiches, which are made while you wait by Taffie Jones. It's also worth visiting on Saturdays for the handmade cakes, and on Sundays for chef Aiko's handmade sushi and Tibetan momos (dumplings).

Temple

French Bakery

APOSTROPHE
3-5 St Bride Street,
London EC4A 4AS
Tel: 020 7353 3708

Main shop and branches: see Oxford Street, page 43

Cheese Shop

INTERNATIONAL CHEESE CENTRE
City Thameslink Station,
Ludgate Hill, London
EC4M 7JH
Tel: 020 7248 4016

Main shop and branches: see City, page 58

French Bakery Pâtisserie

PAUL
147 Fleet Street,
London EC4A 2BU
Tel: 020 7353 5874

147 High Holborn,
London WC2

Main shop and branches: see Covent Garden, page 32

R. TWINING & CO.
216 Strand,
London WC2R 1AP
Tel: 020 7353 3511
Order tel: 0870 241 3667
Fax: 020 7353 5336
Open: Mon-Fri 9.30am-4.30pm **Closed:** Sat, Sun, Bank holidays **Tube:** Aldwych, Temple **Bus:** 4, 11, 15, 23, 26, 76, 171a **Mainline station:** Charing Cross, Blackfriars **Payment:** cash, cheque, Amex, Delta, Maestro, MasterCard, Visa
Mail order

Tea

This narrow little Aladdin's cave of tea, coffee and related paraphernalia occupies the site of a coffee shop founded by Thomas Twining in 1706. The fine tea selection includes limited-edition Keemun and Oolong, plus the very special Rose Pouchong and a Vintage Darjeeling. This shop is the only UK source of this specialist collection, though it is available by mail order. There's a small range of coffee, too, all manner of brewing equipment and a selection of chocolates, including Bendicks.

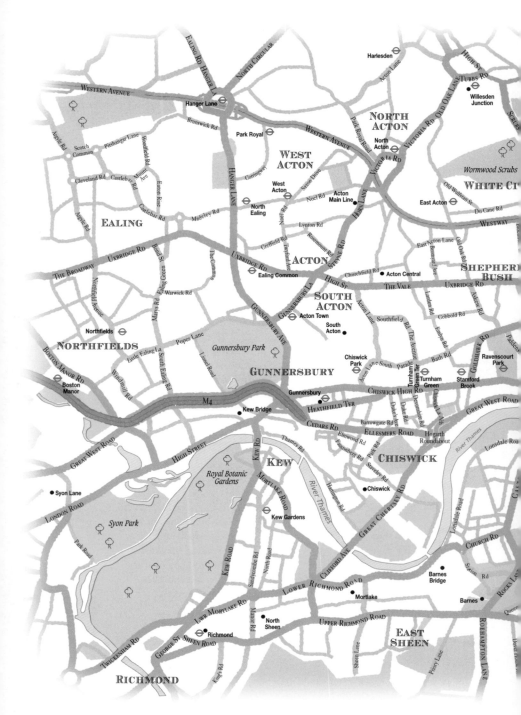

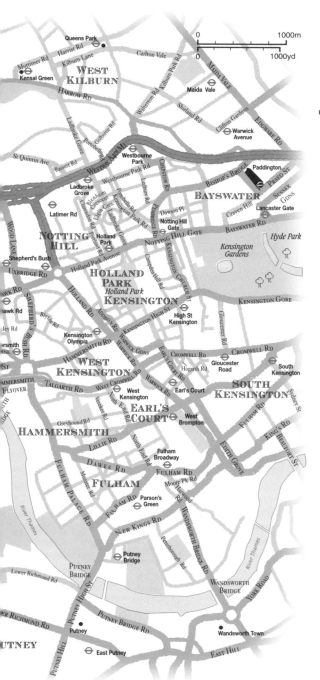

Legend

Motorway

Main Road

Other Road

Highbury &
Islington ● Railway Station

Underground

Waterways

Parks

0   1000m

0   1000yd

Queens Park

Harvest Rd

Kilburn Lane

Carlton Vale

Mortimer Rd

WEST
KILBURN

Kensal Green

HARROW RD

MAIDA VALE

Maida Vale

Walterton Rd

Kilburn Park Rd

Shirland Rd

Clifton Gardens

Warwick
Avenue

EDGWARE RD

WESTWAY (A40 M)

Westbourne
Park

Westbourne Park Rd

CHEPSTOW RD

BISHOP'S BRIDGE

Paddington

PRAED ST

Ladbroke
Grove

Wichholm
Crescent

Elgin Crescent

Kensington Park Rd

Pembridge Rd

Ladbroke Grove

Ledbury Rd

BAYSWATER

Dawson Pl

SUSSEX
GDNS

Latimer Rd

Clarendon Rd

Notting Hill
Gate

Craven Hill

Lancaster Gate

NOTTING
HILL

Holland
Park

NOTTING HILL GATE

KENSINGTON CHURCH ST

BAYSWATER RD

Hyde Park

Shepherd's Bush

Holland Park Avenue

Campden Hill Rd

Kensington
Gardens

UXBRIDGE RD

HOLLAND
PARK

Holland Park

HOLLAND RD

ADDISON RD

KENSINGTON HIGH ST

KENSINGTON GORE

HAWK RD

KENSINGTON

High St
Kensington

SHEPHERD'S BUSH RD

Blythe Rd

Gloucester Rd

hawk Rd

ley Rd

Kensington
Olympia

WARWICK GDNS

CROMWELL RD

CROMWELL RD

rsmith

HAMMERSMITH RD

WARWICK RD

EARL'S COURT RD

Gloucester
Road

South
Kensington

MMERSMITH
FLYOVER

WEST
KENSINGTON

Hogarth Rd

Sydney St

St

TALGARTH RD

WEST CROMWELL RD

WARWICK RD

West
Kensington

Earl's Court

SOUTH
KENSINGTON

FULHAM RD

KING'S RD

BEAUFORT ST

North End Rd

Greyhound Rd

EARL'S
COURT

West
Brompton

HAMMERSMITH

LILLIE RD

North End Rd

EDITH GROVE

Fulham
Broadway

DAWES RD

Munster Rd

FULHAM RD

FULHAM PALACE RD

FULHAM

Moore Pk Rd

Harwood Rd

WANDSWORTH BRIDGE RD

FULHAM RD

Parson's
Green

NEW KINGS RD

Peterborough Rd

River Thames

Putney
Bridge

PUTNEY
BRIDGE

PUTNEY HIGH ST

Lower Richmond Rd

River Thames

WANDSWORTH
BRIDGE

YORK ROAD

PUTNEY
BRIDGE RD

R RICHMOND RD

Putney

UTNEY

PUTNEY HILL

East Putney

Wandsworth Town

EAST HILL

73

Baron's Court

Butcher

H. G. WALTER
51 Palliser Road,
London W14 9EB
Tel: 020 7385 6466
Open: Mon-Fri 8am-7pm, Sat
8am-5pm **Closed:** Sun **Tube:**
Baron's Court **Bus:** 190, 211,
220, 295 **Payment:** cash, cheque,
Amex, Delta, Diner's Card,
MasterCard, Maestro, Visa

This family-owned, Q Guild
butcher was named Best Small
Butcher in Britain in 2002 and
South of England Barbecue
Champion in 2005 – and it's
easy to see why. The counters
positively gleam, and the range
of organic, free-range meat and
poultry is dizzying. You'll find
succulent cuts of Lanarkshire
beef, pork from Surrey's
respected Plantation Pigs and
chicken from Wales's Black
Mountains. The mouth-
watering kebabs, satays,
sausages and steak burgers are
all handmade daily. So, too, are
the popular oven-ready dishes
such as Buffalo Tom – a chicken
breast stuffed with vegetables
and topped with mozzarella,
sun-dried tomatoes and a garlic
marinade. In season, H. G.
Walter stocks a selection of
game to order and, at
Christmas, is the place to go for
superb geese, turkey and honey-
roast ham. Luckily, the friendly
staff, including owner Peter
Heanen's sons Daniel and
Adam, is on hand year-round to
offer guidance. Otherwise, you
might struggle to ever make
a decision.

Chiswick

★ T. ADAMOU & SONS
124-126 Chiswick High Road,
London W4 1PU
Tel: 020 8994 0752
Open: Mon-Sat 8.30am-7pm,
Sun and Bank holidays 9.30am-
2pm **Closed:** 25, 26 Dec. **Tube:**
Turnham Green **Bus:** H91, 27,
237, 267 **Mainline station:**
Chiswick **Payment:** cash, cheque

Cypriot
Greek
Delicatessen
Grocer
Greengrocer

Theodosios Adamou, originally
from Cyprus, opened his
eponymous shop in 1959 and is
credited with bringing the
aubergine to Chiswick. Though
the business is now run on a
day-to-day basis by his sons, he
still keeps a weather eye on it.
Both sides of the entrance are
stacked with fresh fruit and
vegetables, and inside, to the
right, there is always a good
selection of fresh herbs and
salad leaves. You'll find dill,
rocket, mint, purslane, spinach
and curly endive, depending on
the season, plus more specialist
vegetables such as leaf celery
and *kolokassi* for Greek
cooking. Greek bread is
available daily, while on
Tuesdays, Ukrainian rye bread
comes in from a specialist
bakery in Bradford. Alongside
the huge array of dried and
tinned ingredients, and herbs
and spices for Continental and
Asian cookery, the Greek
Cypriot specialities include

cheeses, salted smoked herrings, thick, fresh sheep's yogurt from Cyprus, *bastourma* and *loukanika* sausages, vine leaves in brine, marinated olives, traditional pastries including baklava and *kadaifi*, and packets of nuts galore. There is also a selection of ground Greek coffee and olive oils from Kalamata and Crete, plus a small selection of Greek and Cypriot wines.

Greengrocer

★ ANDREAS GEORGHIOU & CO.

35 Turnham Green Terrace, London W4 1RG
Tel: 020 8995 0140
Fax: 020 8747 0274
E-mail: ageorghiou@aol.com
Website: www.andreasveg.co.uk
Open: Mon-Sat 6am-6pm
Closed: Sun, Bank holidays **Tube:** Turnham Green **Bus:** E3, H91, 237, 267 **Mainline station:** Chiswick **Payment:** cash, cheque, Delta, Maestro, MasterCard, Visa
Wholesake, bespoke delivery

This bustling, jolly shop packs in an impressive range of top-quality fruit and veg, much of which is unique to it. Supplier to The River Café, the Electric Brasserie and Indian restaurant Amaya, among other leading restaurants, Andreas Georghiou & Co. is also frequented by leading food writers and foodie pilgrims from around London, as well as local people. In autumn, the goodies include an impressive range of fresh wild mushrooms, plus squash, globe, Jerusalem artichokes, four different types of garlic, fresh horseradish, an impressive range of salad leaves, *cavolo nero*, Swiss chard, *cime di rapa*, fresh borlotti beans, eight different varieties of potato and Oriental greens. Outside, there's always a wide range of plum and cherry tomatoes, including Sicilian cherry tomatoes on the vine. At Christmas, you'll find white Alba and Périgord truffles, decorated garlic strings and Medjool dates. In the fruit department, there is a good range of apples and pears, including French wax tip pears for poaching, soft fruit in season, plus a variety of exotics. Other temptations include a range of organically grown fruit and veg, dried fruit, prepared spinach, genuine Iranian saffron tips and the shop's now legendary nine-leaf salads.

AS NATURE INTENDED

201 Chiswick High Road, London W4 2DR
Tel: 020 8742 8838
Fax: 020 8742 3131
Website: www.asnatureintended.uk.com
Open: Mon-Fri 9am-8pm, Sat 9am-7pm, Sun 11am-5.30pm
Closed: occasional Bank holidays
Tube: Turnham Green **Bus:** 27, 237, 267 **Mainline station:** Chiswick **Payment:** cash, cheque, Delta, MasterCard, Maestro, Visa

The first totally organic supermarket and past winner of

Wholefood
Organic
Food Hall
Special diet

Organic Retailer of the Year, As Nature Intended is a no-nonsense food store with over 3,500 products offered at competitive prices. The friendly, knowledgeable staff is always willing to help customers without preaching to them – although there is also plenty of in-store information on the benefits of eating organic. Special diets are catered for, as much of the produce is clearly labelled. For the ethical shopper, there is a good range of Fairtrade products, plus an excellent vegan range. On Saturdays, there are usually tastings and demonstrations and a weekly visit from a homeopath. Look out for the freshly squeezed juices and freshly ground coffee, and the delicious bread and cakes from The Celtic Baker.

Branch: see Ealing, page 80

Continental Bakery

BREAD SHOP
296 Chiswick High Road, London W4 1PA
Tel: 020 8747 8443

Branch: see St John's Wood, page 129

Fishmonger

★ COVENT GARDEN FISHMONGERS
37 Turnham Green Terrace, Chiswick, London W4 1RG
Tel: 020 8995 9273
Fax: 020 8742 3899
Open: Tues-Fri 8am-5.30pm, Sat 8am-5pm Closed: Sun, Mon, Bank holidays Tube: Turnham

Green Bus: E3, H91, 27, 237, 267 Mainline station: Chiswick
Payment: cash, cheque, Delta, Maestro, MasterCard, Visa

Phil Diamond runs this family-owned fishmonger, which has been in business for more than 25 years. He stocks an impressive range of fresh fish and seafood, including French *rascasse* and black bream, king and queen scallops, crab, large squid, sparklingly fresh mackerel, swordfish steaks, loin of tuna, red mullet, red snapper and barramundi fillets, and king clip and orange roughy when available. In the shellfish range, you'll find oysters, *palourde*, Venus clams and surf clams, when in season. To survive these days, fishmongers 'have to become entrepreneurs', says Diamond. Accordingly, his range also includes fish-related products, such as fish soup, bouillabaisse, anchovies, smoked fish and Arbroath smokies. He continues to sell fish and seafood at the more expensive end of the market, though; because that's exactly what his customers want.

FISHWORKS
6 Turnham Green Terrace, London W4 1QP
Tel: 020 8994 0086

Main shop: see Marylebone, page 37

Fishmonger

Delicatessen

GROVE PARK DELI

22 Fauconberg Road,
London W4 3JY
Tel/Fax: 020 8995 8219
Open: Mon-Sat 8.30am-5pm,
Sun 8.30am-1pm **Closed:**
Bank holidays **Tube:**
Gunnersbury
Bus: E3, 237, 267, 391
Payment: cash, cheque, Delta,
Maestro, MasterCard, Visa
Catering, food-to-go

Janice Timothy, who trained at
Langan's Brasserie and was
formerly personal chef to
Andrew Lloyd Webber, took
over this friendly and much
appreciated deli in 2003. It
continues to specialize in home-
cooked, main course meals,
including the popular
pissaladière, soups and stuffed
chicken breasts. The range of
dishes and sandwiches is always
growing; you can also savour a
freshly brewed, Monmouth
Coffee Company coffee (page
30) and delicious cake at the
small table outside the shop if
the mood takes you. The deli
sells fine bread from
independent bakeries, as well as
its own focaccia, and an
excellent range of cheeses from
Neal's Yard Dairy (page 31).
You'll also find organic
chocolates, a selection of gift
foods and a fabulous range of
Sicilian honeys, jams and pestos.

INDIGO DELICAFE

98 Turnham Green Terrace,
London W4 1QN
Tel: 020 8995 9000
Fax: 020 8994 5622
Email: indigo.delicafe@virgin.net
Website:
www.indigodelicafe.co.uk
Open: Mon-Fri 9.30am-7pm,
Sat 9am-6pm **Closed:** Sun,
occasional Bank holidays
Tube: Turnham Green **Bus:** E3,
H91, 27, 237, 267 **Mainline**
station: Chiswick **Payment:** cash,
cheque, Delta, Maestro,
MasterCard, Visa
Catering, food-to-go, mail order,
free local delivery

Joseph Viner has spoiled
Chiswick residents with this
wonderful delicatessen, which is
situated within shouting

Delicatessen

66 I like my broccoli small, deep purple before cooking,
and packed with flavour. Fresh broccoli is as pleasurable as
fresh asparagus or an apple plucked from the tree. 99

Monty Don, food writer

distance of Turnham Green tube station. The cool, yellow interior is a treasure trove of products from around the world – the shelves are positively laden with Italian extra virgin olive oils in elegant bottles and beautifully packaged Balsamic vinegars, wines from Italy, English apple juices and liquorice from New Zealand. The stock ranges from everyday essentials to luxury items, so you'll find dried pasta, tinned tomatoes and biscuits nestled alongside Hanbury flavoured sugars and bottles of truffle oil. The deli counter is well stocked with French, English and Italian cheeses, top-grade Parma ham, home-cooked ham, and prepared vegetables and salads. The fridges are also full of home-made pestos, lasagnes, pasta, stuffed and roasted chickens, ready-made sauces and award-winning tiramisus and mince pies – all of which are prepared in the kitchens downstairs. In addition to the deli and café, Indigo also offers a 'dinner tonight' menu and a service called 'bring your own dish', whereby customers can have anything they require prepared in their own dishes, ready to take away and serve up as their own.

Butcher
Free range
Game dealer

MACKEN BROTHERS

44 Turnham Green Terrace,
London W4 1QP
Tel: 020 8994 2646
Open: Mon-Fri 7am-6pm, Sat 7am-5.30pm **Closed:** Sun, Bank holidays **Tube:** Turnham Green

Bus: E3, H91, 27, 237, 267
Mainline station: Chiswick
Payment: cash, cheque, Delta, Maestro, MasterCard, Visa

This butcher stocks high-quality Scotch beef, fine English lamb, free-range poultry, fresh duck legs and breasts, a range of home-made sausages and additive-free and free-range pork, chicken and lamb. You'll also find MacSweens haggis, boned and stuffed quail, flavoured meats for the grill or barbecue, tame and wild French rabbit and game in season, including hare, venison, wild boar (saddles as well as portions) at weekends, diced venison and English veal. At Christmas, the shop stocks Bramble Farm, free-range organic turkeys and Julie Goodman's free-range geese.

★ MAISON BLANC

26-28 Turnham Green Terrace,
London W4 1QP
Tel: 020 8995 7220

French
Bakery
Pâtisserie

Main shop and branches: see St John's Wood, page 132

★ MORTIMER & BENNETT

33 Turnham Green Terrace,
London W4 1RG
Tel: 020 8995 4145
Fax: 020 8742 3068
Website:
www.mortimerandbennett.com
Open: Mon-Fri 8.30am-6.30pm, Sat 8.30am-5.30pm **Closed:** Sun, Bank holidays **Tube:** Turnham Green **Bus:** 27, 37, 267, 391, E3,

Delicatessen
Grocer

H91 **Payment:** cash, cheque, Delta, Maestro, MasterCard, Visa
Free local delivery, mail order

This fabulous delicatessen, run with enthusiasm and passion by Dan Mortimer, is packed with exceptional produce from France, Italy, Spain, Portugal and other Continental countries, as well as the UK. It sells cheeses, charcuterie, hams, preserves, bread, cakes, desserts and much more besides. Seasonal specialities include Christmas puddings from The Carved Angel, stollen and *lebkuchen* from Germany, mini Cheddar truckles from Mull, plus baby Stilton, Lancashire and Cheshire cheeses. The wild smoked salmon comes from Ireland and Scotland. This high-class emporium is surely one of the best delis in London; it has become a selling point amongst the local estate agents and a meeting place for locals who pop in for the regular weekend tastings, where they can also meet the goodies' producers. The shop buys directly from Neal's Yard Dairy (page 31), and also supports small farmers both in the UK and on the Continent. Among the more unusual items, look out for *Saba* (a natural sweetener and flabour enhancer made from the must of Trebbiano or Lambrusco grapes), herby pancetta from Greve in Tuscany and smoked goose wing and goose salame from Udine. Unusual culinary herbs from English nurseries and Italian seeds are fairly new additions. The bread comes from specialist Italian and German bakers, as well as from & Clarke's (page 92) and Poilâne (page 19).

★ THEOBROMA CACAO
Chocolate

43 Turnham Green Terrace, London W4 1RG
Tel: 020 8996 0431
Website: www.theobroma-cacao.co.uk
Open: Mon-Sat 9.30am-6pm, Sun 10.30am-5pm **Closed:** Bank holidays **Tube:** Turnham Green **Bus:** E3, 27, H91, 237, 267, 391
Payment: cash, cheque, Delta, Maestro, Visa

This shop's exotic name derives from the Latin name for the chocolate tree and translates roughly to 'food of the gods'. Indeed, the wide range of handmade chocolates and truffles (which vary in cocoa content from 34-90%) available in this smart, modern shop is impressive. Experienced chefs hand blend their own chocolate to make 120 different goodies. In fact, if it can be made with chocolate, you'll find it here – the shop even sells a range of cosmetics. (Try the cocoa butter massage bars and skin moisturizers with 100% cocoa butter and essential oils, including geranium). The 20-strong range of drinking chocolate is also extremely popular. As an added bonus, with every cup of the fabulous chilli, bergamot, orange or liquorice hot chocolate, you're given a free chocolate from the counter. Value for money is paramount: all chocolates are sold by set box price, so you can fill a box with the most unusual shapes and flavours and still know exactly what you are going to pay.

Ealing

Wholefood
Organic
Food Hall
Special Diet

AS NATURE INTENDED
17-21 High Street,
London W5 5DB
Tel: 020 8840 1404

Main shop: see Chiswick, page 75

Polish
Greek
Grocer
Delicatessen

BRONEK'S DELICATESSEN
124 Northfield Avenue,
London W13 9RT
Tel: 020 8579 2722
Open: Mon-Wed 8am-6.30pm,
Thurs-Sat 8am-7pm **Closed:** Sun
Tube: Northfields **Bus:** E2, E3
Mainline station: West Ealing
Payment: cash, cheque, Delta,
Maestro, MasterCard, Visa

This shop's proprietor, Bronislaw (Bronek) Korwin-Kamienski, is virtually a one-man promotional juggernaut for Polish food in London. When he's not running the shop and preparing its excellent home-made dishes, he provides the catering for Real Ale Festivals across the country, broadcasts on Internet Polish radio, writes a regular cookery column for magazine *Goniec* and gives talks on Polish food. It's

little surprise, then, that the deli is completely given over to Polish and other Eastern European foods. The shelves and counters groan with traditional items including smoked sprats, herrings, cheeses made to Polish highlanders' recipes, a vast array of locally baked bread and Bronek's own *cwikla*, a zesty relish made from beetroot and fresh, grated horseradish. Among the prepared foods, you'll find *bigos*, a delicious hunter's stew made with cabbage, smoked meats, venison, wild mushrooms and wine; cold meats and hams; and a range of wonderfully named sausages. (*Szynka tesciowej*, mother-in-law's ham, and *szynka babuni*, grandmama's ham, are particularly enticing.) Children – and often their parents, as well – adore the shop's chocolate-covered honey cakes, multicoloured lollipops and *powidla*, vanilla-flavoured doughnuts generously filled with puréed prune jam.

★ CARLUCCIO'S
5-6 The Green,
London W5 5DA
Tel: 020 8566 4458

Main shop and branches: see Covent Garden, page 28

RICHARDSON'S FINE FOOD
88 Northfield Avenue,
London W13 9RR
Tel: 020 8567 1064
Fax: 020 8932 0074

Italian
Delicatessen
Café

Butcher
Fishmonger
Game dealer

Portobello
Road Market

Notting Hill – *see page 100*

Brixton Market *– see page 159*

Sri Thai

Shepherd's Bush – *see page 110*

Open: Mon-Thurs 8am-5.30pm, Fri 8am-6pm, Sat 8am-4.30pm
Tube: Northfields **Bus:** E2, E3
Mainline station: West Ealing
Payment: cash, cheque, Delta, Maestro, MasterCard
food-to-go

This award-winning butcher is extremely popular among local residents and has a good range of fresh meats and sausages. (The latter have won the shop gold medals from the North West London Butchers' Association.) Pies can be made to order, and cooked dishes include chicken breasts marinated in green Thai curry. There is a good selection of pâtés, cheeses and game in season. Smoked fish is available, and fresh fish can be supplied upon request.

Branch: 110 South Ealing Road, London W5 4QJ
Tel: 020 8567 4405

THOROGOODS OF EALING
113 Northfield Avenue, London W13 9QR
Tel: 020 8567 0339
Fax: 020 8566 3033
Open: Tues-Sat 8am-5pm
Closed: Sun, Mon **Tube:** Northfields **Bus:** E2, E3 **Mainline station:** West Ealing **Payment:** cash, cheque
Free local delivery, mail order

Established more than 40 years ago, this friendly butcher offers a range of organic meat and free-range poultry. Speciality products include chicken cushions and marinated legs of lamb. There is also a choice of frozen boned and

Butcher
Organic
Free range

North End Road Market

Open: Mon-Sat 8am-6pm **Closed:** Sun **Tube:** Fulham Broadway **Bus:** 14, 28, 74, 190, 195, 391

Fulham, now built up and comparatively 'gentrified', once boasted many market gardens, which perhaps explains the presence of the market which occupies one side of North End Road, south of Lillie Road. Fruit and vegetable stalls make up the largest contingent, with some very good bargains to be had. Some 50-60 stalls stretch along the pavement, off the busy road, and many are beautifully arranged, with superior produce and good-value prices. There is a good fish stall as well, and a few stalls offering household goods.

stuffed ducks, chicken and geese, with a variety of stuffings. The shop's sausages are also very popular, as are its eggs.

Earl's Court

Filipino
Thai
Grocer
Greengrocer

MANILA SUPERMARKET
11 Hogarth Place,
London SW5 0QT
Tel: 020 7373 8305
Open: Mon-Sun 9am-9pm **Tube:** Earls Court **Bus:** 74, 328, C1, C3
Payment: cash, cheque, Amex, Delta, Maestro, MasterCard, Visa

This specialist shop takes a delivery of fresh fruit and vegetables from Thailand and the Philippines every Monday and Friday. It also stocks a wide range of Filipino cooking essentials, from dim sum, spicy pork sausages, spring rolls, prawns and fish to frozen *papaitan*, a local delicacy consisting of tripe, heart and liver. You'll also find a wide selection of frozen leaves, such as pepper, jute, bitter melon and sweet potato; packets of frozen grated *cassava*; a good range of shrimp pastes; jars of salted anchovies, dried shrimp and *ikian bilis*; packets of dried chillies; sweet and sour sauces; chilli pickles; spiced vinegars; noodles; and grains including fragrant, Basmati and Japanese rices.

Fulham

★ COPE'S SEAFOOD
700 Fulham Road,
London SW6 5SA
Tel: 020 7371 7300
Open: Mon-Fri 10am-8pm,
Sat 9am-6pm **Closed:** Sun
Tube: Fulham Broadway,
Parsons Green **Bus:** 14
Payment: cash, cheque, Delta, Maestro, MasterCard, Visa

Fishmonger

Cope's, a wholesale supplier of high-quality fish and seafood, also operates as a traditional fishmonger. Beyond its impressive window display of sparklingly fresh fish and shellfish – most of which come from Cornwall – this efficient, family-run shop sells everything from home-smoked, undyed cod and haddock to smoked cod's roe. You'll also find tasty home-made taramasalata, paella, fish cakes and sushi lunchboxes alongside a vast array of sauces, soups and sea salts.

Branch: see Battersea, page 172

A. A. KING
30A New Kings Road,
London SW6 4ST
Tel: 020 7736 4004
Open: Mon-Fri 7.30am-5.30pm,
Sat 8am-4pm **Closed:** Sun, Bank holidays **Tube:** Parsons Green
Bus: 2 **Payment:** cash, cheque, Delta, Maestro, MasterCard, Visa

Butcher
Free range
Fishmonger

This well-established butcher sells high-quality, free-range meat and has been in business for more than 50 years, though not always on these premises. At first glance, it is rather an ordinary shop. But on closer inspection, a secret goldmine is revealed. Most of A. A. King's lamb comes from the West Country, its pork from Suffolk and its beef from Scotland. The shop makes its own sausages and sells cooked ham and beef, plus marinated meat and poultry ready for grilling. The staff will prepare any speciality cuts to order 'except veggie burgers' and does a roaring trade catering for the races and Henley. The shop also sells fresh fish to order from Billingsgate – including sea bass, John Dory and dressed whole salmon supplied on a board. You'll also find fresh produce, British and Italian sauces, marinades, chutneys and mustards from Wiltshire-based Tracklements, plus biscuits, eggs, stocks and soups. All are sourced from small suppliers.

Delicatessen
Grocer

ELIZABETH KING
34 New Kings Road,
London SW6 4ST
Tel: 020 7736 2826
Fax: 020 7736 9677
Website:
www.elizabethking.com
Open: Mon-Fri 9am-8pm, Sat 9am-6pm, Sun 9am-3.30pm
Closed: Bank holidays and associated Sun **Tube:** Parsons Green **Bus:** 2 **Payment:** cash,

cheque, Amex, Delta, Maestro, MasterCard, Visa
food-to-go

This handy grocer and delicatessen in the heart of Fulham is packed with fresh fruit, vegetables and salad ingredients, bowls of olives and artichoke hearts, dried and fresh pasta, and a good range of rice, oils, and vinegars. It's surely one of the most approachable food shops in London – the friendly, knowledgeable staff knows all of the shop's regulars by name. The local French population has strongly influenced the stock, so you'll find a good selection of *saucissons, madeleines*, Meaux mustard,

> **❝** Even the most enticing fishmonger's display will offer frozen, rather than fresh, prawns. If you are lucky you may find a supply of uncooked ones. Fishmongers who offer such things are to be cherished.
>
> Nigel Slater

jars of *salmis de pintade,* Poilâne bread (page 19), *poulet basquaise* and *coq-au-vin* here, alongside products from Gascony, such as *graisse d'oie.* Other European cuisines are represented among the vast selection of loaves, cakes and pastries by German-style rye bread and Dutch fruit loaves. The speciality cheese section stocks a wide range of British cheeses, including Lincolnshire Poacher, Wedmore, Cashel Blue, Ticklemore goat's cheese, Wigmore, Berkswell and Colston Bassett Stilton. Meanwhile, the shop's recently expanded range of French cheeses boasts such exciting additions as Livarot, Trami d'Alsace and Tomme de Savoie. The also increased range of fresh, pre-packed fish and meat includes Bramble Farm free-range chickens, salt marsh lamb, Plantation Pigs pork and Orkney beef, plus traditional pork sausages and Dorset dry-cured bacon. Holiday specialities include Italian *panettone,* stollen, Easter eggs and handmade chocolates from Browne's and Charbonnel et Walker (page 42). You can also pick up daily essentials such as Neal's Yard Dairy milk and yoghurt (page 31), and a daily-changing menu of delicious takeaway meals.

★ LISBOA DELICATESSEN
6 World's End Place,
London SW10 0HE
Tel: 020 7376 3639

Main shop and branch: see Notting Hill, page 103

Portuguese Delicatessen

★ MAISON BLANC
303 Fulham Road,
London SW10 9QH
Tel: 020 7795 2663

Main shop and branches: see St John's Wood, page 132

French Bakery Pâtisserie

MEGAN'S
571 King's Road,
London SW6 2EB
Tel: 020 7371 7837
Fax: 020 7371 7895
Website: www.megansdeli.com
Open: Mon-Fri 8am-6pm, Sat 9am-6pm **Closed:** Sun, Bank holidays **Tube:** Fulham Broadway
Bus: 14, 22, 28 **Payment:** cash, cheque
Food-to-go, free local delivery

Delicatessen

Situated at the Fulham end of the King's Road, Megan's Deli is a relaxing haven for food lovers. The shelves are laden with high-quality, home-made jams, chutneys, olive oils and biscuits, plus Poilâne bread (page 19). Downstairs, you'll find a charming café, which churns out popular salads, fresh soups and home-made cakes, including wheat- and gluten-free options. You can take these dishes home or eat them at the vast farmhouse table, or in the deli's secluded, walled garden.

Delicatessen
Organic

ONE STOP FRESH

85 Moore Park Road,
London SW6 2DA
Tel: 020 7736 2087
Fax: 020 7731 7412
Website:
www.onestopfresh.com
Open: Mon-Fri 8.30am-4pm
Closed: Sat, Sun, Bank holidays
Tube: Fulham Broadway **Bus:** 11,
14, 22, 211 **Payment:** cash,
cheque (over £10)
**Office catering, food-to-go, café,
mail order, free local delivery**

Situated just yards from Chelsea
football ground, this smart shop
(which was formerly known as
the Moore Park Delicatessen) is
a favourite with Hugh Grant,
Johnny Vaughn and a bevy of
top models. It was established
more than 15 years ago by
Victoria Nixon, herself an ex-
model, and now specializes in
healthy, handmade lunch foods.
The gourmet sandwiches,
including the lip-smackingly
good organic chicken with
lemon mayonnaise and fresh
basil, are all made with artisanal
bread, rolls and baguettes. You'll
also find delicious, freshly made
soups and a selection of five
different prepared salads each
day. Other guilt-free enticements
include hand-carved Alderton
hams on the bone, green olive
pâté, smoked salmon and a
range of biscuits and chocolates
that contain no added sugar. The
organic, individually portioned
ready meals are also very
popular – particularly among
'busy housewives, late-night City

workers, singletons and cheating
dinner hosts', notes Nixon. With
its elegant design and friendly,
enthusiastic staff, this shop is
always a pleasure to visit.

★ PLANET ORGANIC

25 Effie Road,
London SW6 1EL
Tel: 020 7731 7222

Wholefood
Organic
Food Hall

Main shop and branches: see
Bayswater, page 16

PRIMA

192 North End Road,
London W14 9NX
Tel: 020 7385 2070
Open: Mon-Thurs and Sat
9.30am-6pm, Fri 9.30am-7pm
Closed: Sun, Bank holidays **Tube:**
West Kensington **Payment:** cash,
cheque

Polish
Delicatessen

This simple, family-run Polish
deli has been in business for
more than 20 years and is a real
treasure trove – especially for
the Polish community in
neighbouring Hammersmith. It
stocks every kind of Polish
delicacy, including pickled
mushrooms, *sauerkraut*,
cucumbers in brine, jars of
beetroot, rollmops and salted
herring fillets. Smoked bacon
and sausages are also popular,
and you'll find strings of
kabanos hanging up inside the
shop. The baked goods –
including Ukrainian rye bread,
cakes, fresh Polish doughnuts
and delicious chocolate-covered
plums – are made by the
family's own bakery. Prima also

carries a good range of Polish beers and flavoured vodkas. Don't leave without buying a bottle of either the lemon- or pepper-flavour vodka.

Butcher
Organic
Delicatessen
Grocer

★ RANDALLS
113 Wandsworth Bridge Road, London SW6 2TE
Tel: 020 7736 3426
Open: Mon-Fri 8.30am-5.30pm, Sat 7am-4pm **Closed:** Sun **Tube:** Fulham Broadway **Bus:** 14, 22, 28, 195 **Payment:** cash, cheque, Amex, Delta, Maestro, MasterCard, Visa

Brian Randall knows many of his customers on a first-name basis, as he has been based here for well over a decade, selling high-quality meats and delicatessen goods. If you want the meat to be boned or cut for you in a special way, this is accomplished with good grace and at high speed by skilled hands. Around 30% of the meat and poultry is organic, with the majority of the rest free range. Randalls sources its naturally reared beef from Inverurie (Aberdeen Angus or cross – cuts include rib and rolled fillet), with the lamb from the West Country. Dinner-party presentation cuts of lamb such as crown roast or guard of honour are always available, as are saddle of lamb, rack of lamb, stuffed rolled leg of pork, marinated chicken pieces, home-made sausages, venison and wild boar. The shop also carries game in season, as well

as MacSweens haggis. The cheese counter is well-stocked with British and Continental fare, including Bosuth Ash, English goat's cheese and seasonal Vacherin. You'll also find a range of home-made preserves and biscuits to go with them, plus German bread. Kelly Bronze turkeys are available at Christmas. Gordon Ramsay says this is the best butcher in London.

Hammersmith

BUCHANAN'S ORGANIC DELICATESSEN
22 Aldensley Road, London W6 ODH
Tel: 020 8741 2138
Open: Mon-Sat 7am-6pm, Sun 8am-2pm
Closed: 25-27 Dec., 1-2 Jan., occasional Bank holidays
Tube: Hammersmith, Ravenscourt Park **Bus:** 190, 267, 271, 391 **Payment:** cash, cheque, Amex, Maestro, MasterCard, Visa

Grocer
Greengrocer
Organic

Owned and run by the Buchanan family, this corner shop is situated directly opposite Stenton Family Butchers (page 88). Most of the foods on offer are organic. You'll find dairy goods, including ice cream and goat's butter; delicatessen items (honey-roasted and smoked hams, salume, chorizo etc.); plus coffee, tea, biscuits, cereals, nuts and grains, honeys, oils, vinegars, pulses, pasta, dried mushrooms, pickles and sea vegetables. There is also a range of baby food, which makes the place popular with young families. In the morning, the bread table groans with freshly baked loaves, and the fridge is well stocked with vegetables and salad ingredients. The shop's range of cheeses – which includes Quicke's mature Cheddar, Wessex goat's cheese, Godmister vintage Cheddar, Duddleswell sheep's cheese, organic halloumi, extra mature Gouda and pecorino sardo – is somewhat eclectic. Proprietor Alice Buchanan notes that if a customer requests a cheese that Buchanan's doesn't stock, she is very happy to order it in on a trial basis. With its own coffee shop – where a comfy sofa, reading matter, freshly made soups and sandwiches, and great savoury and sweet pastries supplied by The Homemade Food Company await – this is a great local amenity.

BUSHWACKER WHOLEFOODS

Wholefood
Organic

132 King Street,
London W6 0QU
Tel: 020 8748 2061
Open: Mon and Wed-Sat
9.30am-6pm, Tues 10am-6pm
Closed: Sun, Bank holidays **Tube:**
Hammersmith, Ravenscourt
Park **Bus:** 27, 190, 267, 391, H91
Payment: cash, cheque, Delta,
Maestro, MasterCard, Visa
Food-to-go

The owners of this wholefood shop, which stocks a large range of organic and natural foods, are renowned for their staunch campaigning on food issues. There is a good selection of vegetarian cheeses and organic fruit and veg. Apples and apple juice are delivered direct from Crones Orchard in Norfolk, and honey comes from Green Bees' apiaries.

THE OLIVE BAR DELI

Delicatessen

140 Shepherds Bush Road,
London W6 7PB
Tel: 020 7603 5717
Open: Mon-Fri 8am-6pm, Sat
8.30-5pm, Sun 9am-3pm **Tube:**
Hammersmith **Bus:** 72, 295, 220,
283 **Payment:** cash, cheque,
Amex, Delta, Maestro,
MasterCard, Visa
Catering

This wonderful deli, formerly Sutherlands Fine Food and Wine, is something of an oasis on the Shepherds Bush Road – and is now owned by Pete Dodwell and Max Page. Its windows are stacked high with freshly baked bread (focaccia, rye, soda, *pugliese*, sourdough, to name just a few) on one side and cakes (Tunisian orange and almond), croissants, pâtisserie and savoury pastries on the other. The deli counter sells pâtés, *rillettes*, salads, cheeses, hams, salume and dips, and at the table opposite you'll find huge bowls of olives and marinated vegetables. The fridges are laden with Neal's Yard Dairy produce (page 31), fresh herbs, Martin Pitt free-range eggs and French cakes and *tartes*. At Christmas, you'll find truckles of Neal's Yard Dairy cheeses, Ackermans chocolates (page 134), marrons glacés, superior *panettone* and other seasonal goodies. The shop also stocks a good range of organic tea and coffee; organic olive oils, vinegars and pasta; and a carefully chosen selection of French wines and spirits.

Butcher
Organic
Free range
Game dealer

STENTON FAMILY BUTCHERS
55 Aldensley Road,
London W6 0DH
Tel: 020 8748 6121
Open: Tues, Wed and Fri 8am-6.30pm, Thurs 8am-1pm, Sat 8am-5pm **Closed:** Mon, Sun
Tube: Hammersmith, Ravenscourt Park **Bus:** 190, 267, 271, 391 **Payment:** cash, cheque

This traditional butcher, run for 40 years by owner and licenced game dealer John Stenton, specializes in free-range and organic meat, including Welsh Black Beef, Gloucester Old Spot, Blue pork (a cross between wild boar and traditional pork) and welfare-reared veal. It is also renowned for its range of handmade, organic pork, lamb and beef sausages, which includes four wheat-free pork varieties. All of the meat is traceable, as you can see from the list posted behind the counter. Stenton also stocks Orkney Pâtés, the full range of the Rannoch Smokery products and fine pies with organic pastry

by The Handmade Pie Company. (The latter range includes Gloucester Old Spot pork with apple chutney pie; pork, apricot and ginger pie; and chicken and spinach pie.) A friendly and enthusiastic shop, Stenton is always well worth a visit.

Holland Park

JEROBOAMS
96 Holland Park Avenue,
London W11 3RB
Tel: 020 7727 9359
Fax: 020 7792 3672
Website: www.jeroboams.co.uk
Open: Mon-Fri 8am-8pm, Sat 8.30am-7pm, Sun 10am-5pm
Tube: Holland Park, Notting Hill Gate **Bus:** 94 **Payment:** cash, cheque, Amex, Maestro, MasterCard, Visa
Catalogue, mail order

This shop and its Belgravia branch specialize in the finest cheeses from the UK, Ireland and Continental Europe, with artisanal French cheese the real focus. It has its own maturing rooms, and the knowledgeable assistants work as *affineurs*, supervising the maturing themselves. Some 160 varieties, some very unusual, are stocked, including sheep's cheese from the Azores, unpasteurized Cheddar-style Lincolnshire Poacher and *Tête de Moine*. You can even buy a traditional *girolle* on which to serve

Cheese Shop
Delicatessen

Yasar Halim

Harringay – *see page 140*

Carluccio's

Covent Garden – *see page 28*

C. Lidgate

Holland Park – *see page 89*

& Clarke's

Kensington – *see page 92*

Maison Blanc

St John's Wood branch – *see page 132*

your choice. Jeroboams also stocks a range of goodies including goose confit, oils, vinegars, charcuterie, speciality bread, coffee, caviar, wines and champagnes. Hampers and gift boxes are especially popular at Christmas, and as well as cheeses include biscuits, chutneys, smoked salmon and other delicacies.

Branch: see Belgravia, page 18

Butcher
Organic
Free range
Game Dealer
Grocer

★ **C. LIDGATE**
110 Holland Park Avenue,
London W11 4UA
Tel: 020 7727 8243
Fax: 020 7229 7160
Open: Mon-Fri 7am-6pm,
Sat 7am-5pm **Closed:** Sun, Bank
holidays **Tube:** Holland Park
Bus: 49, 94, 295 **Payment:** cash,
cheque, Amex, Delta, Maestro,
MasterCard, Visa
**Bespoke delivery, delivery,
mail order**

David Lidgate is in the fourth generation of his family to run this butchery business, which was established by his great-grandfather in 1850. It is justly known as a top-rate butcher, as a raft of awards proudly displayed on the walls attests. No growth promoters, hormones or antibiotics are used in the rearing of the meat stocked here, much of which is organic or organically fed – and animal welfare is a priority. The shop's motto is 'naturally grown, naturally fed'. Among the organic meats on offer are

> **❝** There are certain rules of thumb when buying meat. Find out about the maturation history of the meat and ask where it comes from. Understand that quality is about balancing taste and texture. The muscles that work hardest have the most flavour but need to be cooked differently. Finally, does the product look good? **❞**
>
> David Lidgate, Master Butcher

beef and lamb from Prince Charles's farm at Highgrove, Gloucester Old Spot pork from Gatcombe Park, the home of the Princess Royal, and pure-bred Aberdeen Angus beef. The chicken is sourced from a variety of suppliers: the free-range birds come from Suffolk Farms, while the organic ones come from Kelly's. A wide range of hams, pâtés and quiches are made on the premises – and the selection of handmade sausages is huge. You'll find some truly unusual flavours, such as chicken korma, to tempt the tastebuds, as well as old favourites. The pies, for which the shop has been named National Pie Champion, are also home-made and worth a special mention. They are prepared daily with fresh vegetables, home-made butter-based pastry and good cuts of meat, and range from traditional steak and kidney (Egon Ronay's favourite) and game pie to *boeuf bourgignon* and lamb, leek and apricot. Excellent cheeses are always available, including organic varieties. In the autumn and at Christmas you can order game birds and bronze turkeys. If you are stocking up for a barbeque, there is no need to shop elsewhere: C. Lidgate even sells gluten-free vegetarian burgers. You'll also find a range of ready meals, which are also available in children's mini sizes, plus organic baby foods. This is Nigella Lawson's favourite butcher.

★ MAISON BLANC

102 Holland Park Avenue,
London W11 4UA
Tel: 020 7221 2494

French
Bakery
Pâtisserie

Main shop and branches: see
St John's Wood, page 132

★ MICHANICOU BROTHERS

2 Clarendon Road,
London W11 3AA
Tel: 020 7727 5191
Fax: 020 7243 5719
Open: Mon-Fri 9am-6.30pm,
Sat 9am-5.30pm **Closed:** Sun,
Bank holidays
Tube: Holland Park **Bus:** 94
Payment: cash, cheque
Delivery

Greengrocer
Organic

An independent greengrocer is a rare phenomenon, but that's not the only reason this small shop, which is reported to be John Cleese's local, deserves to be patronized. Don't be phased by the huge, chaotic array of exotic fruit and vegetables displayed on the floor-to-ceiling shelves. In addition to the basics, you can find a large range of squashes – acorn, spaghetti, blue and yellow onion – as well as pumpkins, sweet potatoes, Japanese mustard cress, yellow Dutch courgettes, French Jerusalem artichokes, cardoons, oxheart and Italian tomatoes, Kenyan jalapeño chillies, lemon grass,

SUMMERILL & BISHOP

100 Portland Road, London W11 4LN
Tel: 020 7221 4566

 In the Area This fabulous, French-influenced kitchen shop sits comfortably in the area known as Clarendon Cross, alongside some of London's most innovative and famous boutiques, not to mention bars, cafés and restaurants. After a lunch at Julie's, perhaps, or an afternoon spent browsing at The Cross, pop in for high-quality tableware and kitchenware, including handmade chopping boards, designer Italian kitchen gadgets and antique French linen, glasses and china.

strings of smoked garlic, as well as several varieties of wild mushrooms and white truffles. The two friendly Greek Cypriot owners pride themselves on stocking seasonal produce from all corners of the globe, and the fruit selection doesn't disappoint, either. You'll find quinces from Turkey, golden kiwis from New Zealand, Colombian gooseberries, Israeli strawberries, pomegranates, kumquats, custard apples, persimmons, sharon fruit, Thai mangosteens – a sort of sherbety lychee – and the unusual *sapodillo* or *chico* from India, which has a texture like kiwi and a taste of brown sugar. There is also an assortment of nuts, plus boxes of Italian free-range eggs. If you are after organic produce, visit on Wednesday, when the best that is to be found in the markets is delivered.

French
Pâtisserie

RENAISSANCE

108 Holland Park Avenue,
London W11 4UA
Tel: 020 7221 3598
Fax: 020 7221 4477
Open: Mon-Sun 7.30am-8pm
Closed: 25 Dec. **Tube:** Holland Park **Bus:** 94 **Payment:** cash, cheque, Maestro, MasterCard, Visa
Catering

This family-run café-brasserie is a favourite among local residents and office workers, who crowd its outdoor tables at lunch- and dinnertime. Baguette sandwiches, salads,

croissants and viennoiserie are freshly made each day and can either be taken away or enjoyed on the premises with a cup of coffee or a glass of wine. The desserts, which can also be taken away in individual portions, are difficult to resist. Choose from vanilla cassis, *tarte au citron* or the undisputed star of the show: the rich, French classic gateau *Opéra*, a dark chocolate layered biscuit cake soaked in coffee, chocolate and praline mousse.

SPECK

2 Holland Park Terrace,
Portland Road,
London W11 4ND
Tel/Fax: 020 7229 7005
Website: www.speck-deli.co.uk
Open: Daily 9am-8pm **Closed:** Sun, Bank holidays **Tube:** Holland Park **Bus:** 94 **Payment:** cash, cheque, Amex, Maestro, MasterCard, Visa
Catering, food-to-go

This chic Italian deli offers a broad range of food-to-go. In addition to the tortelloni filled with fresh spinach or porcini mushrooms, and the ready-to-bake cannelloni and lasagna, the shop will make any kind of risotto to order. Other delicious home-made specialities include fresh soups; Napoletana, tomato and aubergine, and cream and mushroom pasta sauces; and desserts such as chocolate mousse with amaretti or *panna cotta*. The *traiteur* counter is well stocked with

Italian
Delicatessen

delicacies including *risotto al pesto, involtini* of speck (smoked ham cured in the Dolomites and wrapped round thin French bean parcels), marinated artichokes, and basil and rocket pestos. There is also a wide variety of Italian cheeses, cold meats and unusual salume, which the helpful staff allows you to taste. For a special occasion, treat yourself to an elaborately decorated box of *panettone* or *pandoro*. The dried pasta, preserves, extra virgin olive oils, Balsamic vinegars and vintage Italian wines are also worth considering.

Kensington

Italian
Delicatessen
Café

★ CARLUCCIO'S
1-5 Old Brompton Road,
London SW7 3HZ
Tel: 020 7581 8101

Main shop and branches: see
Covent Garden, page 28

Bakery
Pâtisserie
Delicatessen

★ & CLARKE'S
122 Kensington Church Street,
London W8 4BH
Tel: 020 7229 2190
Fax: 020 7229 4564
Website: www.sallyclarke.com
Open: Mon-Fri 8am-8pm, Sat
8am-4pm **Closed:**
Sun, Bank
holidays
Tube:
Notting
Hill
Gate **Bus:**
27, 28, 31,
52, 70, 94,

328 **Payment:** cash, cheque,
Amex, Delta, Maestro,
MasterCard, Visa
Mail order

This treasure trove of a shop is attached to Sally Clarke's award-winning restaurant and offers a range of foods that are produced in its kitchen. The 35 types of bread are its speciality, however. These are also sold wholesale: up to 2,000 hand-shaped loaves are made every night and sold to shops, restaurants and even Carluccio's. You'll find the justly famous rosemary and raisin, oatmeal honeypot, and fig and fennel loaves, plus a wide selection of rye, sourdough, French and Italian bread. Cakes – the rich chocolate cake is especially delicious – and & Clarke's own-brand shortbread are also made on the premises. The hand-rolled bitter chocolate truffles are to die for, as are the spiced nuts and buttery oat biscuits. Try the pastes for hot drinks, including Sicilian almond milk paste, *Gianduia* (a delicious chocolate-hazelnut paste from Bra in Italy) and *Cioccolato Modicano* (a 100% pure cocoa paste with cinnamon and vanilla – melt it in hot milk). Freshly baked pizza, focaccia and pastries are available to take away or eat in. Some items, such as fresh herbs or home-made mayonnaise are not always displayed, so ask on the day for availability. There is also a wide selection of fruit, vegetables, butters, Neal's Yard Dairy cheeses (page 31), preserves, pickles, relishes, pasta sauces, olives and olive oils, and a small café space at the back.

Fishmonger

THE FISH SHOP AT KENSINGTON PLACE
201 Kensington Church Street, London W8 7LX
Tel: 020 7243 6626
Fax: 020 7243 6627
Open: Tues-Fri 9am-7pm, Sat 9am-5pm **Closed:** Mon, Sun, Bank holidays
Tube: Notting Hill Gate **Bus:** 27, 28, 31, 52, 70, 94, 328
Payment: cash, cheque, Amex, Delta, Maestro, MasterCard, Visa
Catering, free local delivery

Part of the successful Kensington Place restaurant directly next door, this small fishmonger stocks a full range of British coastal fish, as well as good-quality tuna and swordfish. Seafood includes lobster, scallops, oysters, squid and mussels. The shelves are laden with extra virgin olive oils, vinegars and a small range of ready-prepared fish pies and fish cakes. The staff guarantees the freshness of the shop's produce by buying only whole fish from day boats and will clean and fillet anything for you upon request.

★ MAISON BLANC
7A Kensington Church Street, London W8 4LF
Tel: 020 7937 4767

Main shop and branches: see St John's Wood, page 132

French
Bakery
Pâtisserie

MILLER OF KENSINGTON
14 Stratford Road, London W8 6QD
Tel: 020 7937 1777
Fax: 020 7938 2882
Open: Mon and Sat 8am-1.30pm, Tues-Fri 8am-6pm
Closed: Sun, Bank holidays **Tube:** Olympia, High Street Kensington **Bus:** 9, 10, 27, 28, 31, 49 **Payment:** cash, cheque, Delta, Maestro, MasterCard, Visa
Catering, local delivery

Mohamed el Banna has been in business here for over 15 years, selling exclusively organic meat. Miller's is one of the few butchers in London to boast its own cold store, in which meat is hung for a minimum of two weeks. At Christmas, you'll find the famous Victorian Royal Roast, a goose stuffed with duck, which in turn is stuffed with pheasant, then chicken, partridge and quail – all boned. Also popular is the shop's own 'Fait Maison' range of vacuum-packed, home-made ready meals, which include the likes of ready-marinated shoulder of lamb and vegetables. El Banna's Egyptian origins are reflected in some of the Middle Eastern specialities that are on offer

Middle
Eastern
Organic
Butcher
Delicatessen

here, including trays of baklava, cow's milk feta cheese and an Egyptian hard cheese made from buffalo milk. You'll also find large bowls of marinated olives, quail eggs, haggis, smoked duck breast, smoked Scotch salmon and organic free-range eggs. Tins of Egyptian *ful medames* beans, jars of French soup and duck gizzard confit, Italian pasta and sauces, chutneys, and a large selection of cold-pressed extra virgin olive oils also adorn the shelves.

French
Pâtisserie

PÂTISSERIE VALERIE
27 Kensington Church Street, London W8 4LL
Tel: 020 7937 9574

Main shop and branches: see Soho, page 54

Iranian
Pâtisserie
Grocer
Greengrocer
Delicatessen

★ REZA PÂTISSERIE
345 Kensington High Street, London W8 6NW
Tel: 020 7602 3674/7603 4924
Fax: 020 7610 4221
Open: Mon-Sun 9am-8.30pm
Closed: Christmas **Tube:** Kensington Olympia, West Kensington **Bus:** 9, 10, 27, 28, 49 **Payment:** cash, cheque

Reza Pâtisserie carries a little bit of everything Iranian, from pickles to ice cream to pricey tins of Beluga caviar. But it is the seductive scent of rosewater and roast pistachios – and the dual displays of roast nuts and melon seeds on the one side of the shop, and myriad sweet pastries on the other – that will entice you in. The shop offers at least 30 varieties of pastry at any one time. All are freshly baked on the premises and, somewhat disconcertingly, are unnamed – partly because the selection changes all the time, and partly because non-Iranians would find most names meaningless. The staff is more than helpful, however, and will happily explain the products and talk you through, for instance, the role of saffron-scented crystal sugar in treating stomach upsets. In terms of what to buy: your best bet is to ask for a selection box of pastries. Weighing in at half a kilo, it costs surprisingly little but is full of delights.

★ SUPER BAHAR
349a Kensington High Street, London W8 6NW
Tel: 020 7603 5083
Open: Mon-Sun 9am-8.30pm
Closed: Bank holidays **Tube:** Kensington Olympia, West Kensington **Bus:** 9, 10, 27, 28, 49 **Payment:** cash, cheque

Iranian
Grocer
Greengrocer

Super Bahar describes itself as a purveyor of Middle Eastern/Oriental/Continental food, but in truth it is an Iranian grocery and greengrocery par excellence. Indeed, it is something of an Iranian cultural centre: one wall is lined with videos, cassettes and cookbooks, and Iranian music plays uncompromisingly in the background. You will find freeze-dried herbs and exotic spice mixtures, including *zatar, sumak,* and sour grape, lime and yoghurt powders, plus pomegranate and morello cherry syrups, dried sour apricots, dried barberries, barberry paste and lemon-salted pistachios. Other staples include roast chickpea flour, pickled garlic cloves and scented waters. Saffron, too, is available in everything from small sachets to beautifully scripted caskets. Super Bahar is also, famously, London's prime over-the-counter source of wholesale-priced Iranian caviar. No credit cards are accepted, so you will need to fill your pockets with wads of notes before you visit.

Notting Hill

Portuguese
Pâtisserie

CAFÉ OPORTO

62A Golborne Road,
London W10 5PS
Tel: 020 8968 8839
Open: Mon-Sun 8am-7pm
Closed: 25, 26 Dec., 1 Jan. and
Bank holidays **Tube:** Ladbroke
Grove, Westbourne Park **Bus:** 7,
23, 28, 31, 52, 70, 295, 302
Payment: cash, cheque

This small café, which specializes in Portuguese cakes and pastries, is always bursting with people inside and out – proof of the high quality of its fare. You'll also find savoury rolls of fish fillet, home-made roast pork and chicken escalopes, typical *rissois de camarao* (prawns in a white,

creamy sauce encased in a pastry case), *croquetes de carme* (fried pastry croquettes of beef) and the traditional *pasteis de bacalhau* (salt cod fish cakes). Most of the typical *pasteis de nata, queijadas, bolos de feijao, bolos de arroz* and *bolos de coco* are made in Café Oporto's bakery in south London, but Maria, wife of the owner, Sebastian da Corte, is renowned for her home-made *pudim de caramelo* and a type of pineapple jelly flan, which those in the know travel miles to buy. Equally delicious is the *Jesuita,* a flaky pastry cake with almonds, custard cream and cinnamon, and a French-style apple tart, which is filled with generous slivers of apple and custard cream on a biscuit pastry base.

★ CHALMERS & GRAY

67 Notting Hill Gate,
London W11 3JS
Tel: 020 7221 6177
Fax: 020 7727 3907
Open: Mon-Fri 8am-6pm, Sat
8am-5pm **Closed:** Sun, Bank
holidays **Tube:** Notting Hill
Gate **Bus:** 12, 27, 28, 31, 52, 70,
94, 302, 328 **Payment:** cash,
cheque, Delta, Maestro,
MasterCard, Visa
Free delivery

This excellent fishmonger's fresh fish and shellfish are brought in from the major Scottish and English ports daily and are beautifully arranged and iced on a huge marble slab,

Fishmonger

95

creating a display that looks rather like an impressionist painting. You will find fresh tuna, cod fillet, sea bass, salmon and sole alongside oysters, crab, lobster and langoustines that are boiled on the premises. Chalmers & Gray also stocks caviar, smoked salmon, smoked cod's roe and free-range chickens. Owner John Gray is more than happy to order special items such as carp or pike, which are not normally stocked, and will also accept accounts.

Spanish
Delicatessen
Grocer

P. DE LA FUENTE

288 Portobello Road,
London W10 5TE
Tel/Fax: 020 8960 5687
Open: Mon-Sat 9am-6pm
Closed: Sun, Bank holidays **Tube:** Ladbroke Grove **Bus:** 7, 23, 28, 52, 70, 295 **Payment:** cash, cheque, Amex, Delta, Maestro, MasterCard, Visa

P. de la Fuente was established near the flyover more than 30 years ago and is still a favourite haunt among London's Spanish expats. They come for typically Spanish staples such as extra virgin olive oil, smoked paprika, tripe with chickpeas, *fabada* (a peasant stew from Asturias) and cider, wine and sherry vinegars. The selection of tinned olives is enormous – there are black and green

ones in various sizes and forms, including plain, pitted and stuffed with anchovies, pimentos, lemon, chilli or cheese. Saffron strands are available in packets, already ground, and in boxes and tiny, handblown glass bottles with cork stoppers. At Christmas, Spanish sweetmeats, such as *turron* (Spanish nougat with nuts and almonds) make their appearance. The deli counter at the rear of the shop offers a good choice of salume, chorizos, cured cold meats, *morcilla*, cured Serrano ham and Spanish *bacalao* (dried salt cod), and the cheeses include a variety of *cabras* and manchegos at various stages of maturation. Be sure to sample the delicious loose olives and soaked, dried beans – and just try to leave without buying one of the lovely terracotta pots stacked in towers against the wall.

FELICITOUS

19 Kensington Park Road,
London W11 2EU
Tel: 020 7243 4050
Fax: 020 7243 4052
Open: Mon-Fri 9am-9pm, Sat 9am-7pm, Sun 10am-5pm
Closed: 25, 26 Dec., 1 Jan. **Tube:** Notting Hill Gate, Ladbroke Grove **Bus:** 7, 23, 27, 28, 31, 52, 70, 328 **Payment:** cash, cheque, Amex, Electron, MasterCard, Solo, Visa
Catering, gift baskets to order, delivery, food-to-go

Delicatessen

Despite stiff competition from nearby Mr Christian's (page 104), Felicitous more than holds its own. Its selection of De Gustibus organic bread (page 36) tends to sell out in the first half hour of the day. Among the preserves, Wendy Brandon's and Martin des Pyrénées' handmade conserves, Escoffier's Sweet Pepper Chutney in kilner jars and the pottery jars of *Mel de Montanya* stand out. Own-brand products include extra virgin olive oil, muesli, a large range of cakes, gold chocolate dragées and cocoa-dusted almonds. Indeed, Felicitous is big on its chocolates, which are mostly made by Valrhona and are supplied by The Chocolate Society (page 18). The well-stocked deli counter offers a range of cheeses from Neal's Yard Dairy (page 31) and various European suppliers; Tuscan wild boar, rosemary, truffle and fennel salamis; cooked and dried hams; and big bowls of vegetables and marinated and stuffed olives. The *traiteur* dishes, which are cooked on the premises daily, are a speciality and include such tasty dishes as turnip and chive soup with organic bread, saffron risotto, chicken pesto and salmon fish cakes.

Food Hall
Organic

★ **FRESH & WILD**
210 Westbourne Grove,
London W11 2RH
Tel: 020 7229 1063
Fax: 020 7243 0988

Website: www.freshandwild.com
Open: Mon-Sat 8am-8pm, Sun 11am-7pm **Closed:** 25, 26 Dec., 1 Jan. **Tube:** Bayswater, Notting Hill Gate **Bus:** 7, 23, 27, 70
Payment: cash, cheque, Delta, Maestro, MasterCard, Visa
Catering, delivery, food-to-go

This past winner of the Soil Association's Organic Best Large Store award stocks a wide range of organic products. Established in 1998, it has built up an excellent reputation for giving customers advice on their products, food allergies and herbal remedies. (The shop's assistants are all specially trained.) You'll find organic produce, dairy products, fish and meat; a good selection of beers and wines; and copious store-cupboard items including cereals, herbal tea, speciality oils and dried fruit and nuts. Fresh bread and hot dishes are prepared in a central, certified organic kitchen and delivered daily to this store and its branches. The food-to-go is mainly vegetarian and vegan, and includes soups, salads, tagines, dals and other deliciously healthy items. You can also eat in next door.

Branches: see Battersea, page 173, Camden, page 115, Shoreditch, page 65, Soho, page 52, Stoke Newington, page 149

BOOKS FOR COOKS

4 Blenheim Crescent, London W11 1NN
Tel: 020 7221 1992 **Fax:** 020 7221 1517
Website: www.booksforcooks.com
Open: Tues-Sat 10am-6pm **Closed:** Mon,
Sun, 3 weeks August, 10 days Christmas,
Bank holidays
Mail order, lunch, coffee and cakes available

In the Area There is cookery in the air as well as on the shelves of this unique bookshop, which stocks nearly 8,000 food-related titles. Now owned by Rosie Kindersley and Eric Treuillé and completely refurbished, the shop has become the ultimate destination for anyone interested in cooking and eating well, as well as functioning as a meeting place and information exchange for chefs and others in the food industry. More like a food lovers' club than a shop, it is staffed by friendly enthusiasts and managed by Sally Hughes. Recipes from the books are tested daily in the little kitchen and can be sampled at one of the tables in the adjacent café area at the back. Upstairs there is now a custom-built demonstration kitchen for the modestly priced and very popular cookery workshops, which take place throughout the year (contact the shop for details).

Spanish
Delicatessen
Grocer

★ R. GARCIA & SONS

248-250 Portobello Road,
London W11 1LL
Tel: 020 7221 6119
Fax: 020 7229 9635
Open: Mon-Sat 9am-6.30pm,
Sun 10am-6pm **Tube:** Notting
Hill Gate, Ladbroke Grove **Bus:**
7, 23, 28, 52, 70, 295 **Payment:**
cash, cheque, Amex, Delta,
Maestro, MasterCard, Visa

This delightful and very Spanish shop has been in the Garcia family for three generations and has long been a place of pilgrimage for Spanish food lovers. The shelves are crammed full of Spanish and Mediterranean produce – you'll find tins of olives, artichokes, eggplants, palm hearts, sardines, mussels, snails and squid, not to mention dried pulses and beans, chick peas and a large selection of pasta. The cold cabinet is well stocked with dried salt cod and marinated anchovies. But it is really the deli counter, which spans the width of the shop at the rear, that draws customers such as fellow deli-owner Tom Conran. Here, giant Serrano hams sway from the ceiling, while below, customers can choose from a large range of sausages, *morcillas*, salamis, chorizos, cured cold meats and dried hams. Sweet acorn-fed ham is a speciality. The cheeses are equally enticing; there are *cabras* and manchegos at all stages of maturation, plus smoked *Idiazabal*, made with sheep's milk. Be sure to try the many varieties of marinated olives, which come dry, fleshy and stuffed. The huge range of typically Spanish sweetmeats includes *turron* (Spanish nougat with almonds and nuts), boxes of *polvoron* biscuits and the divine *alfajores almendras* (with almonds, honey and cinnamon). Worth noting, too, is the range of European extra virgin olive oils. Once you've finished shopping, you can now also enjoy a rejuvenating glass of wine or a cup of *café con leche* – with some tortillas or tapas, of course – at next door's Café Garcia, which opened in 2004.

Fishmonger

GOLBORNE FISHERIES
75 Golborne Road,
London W10 5NP
Tel: 020 8960 3100
Fax: 020 8948 8956
Open: Mon 10am-4pm, Tues-Sat 8.30am-6pm **Closed:** Sun, Bank holidays **Tube:** Ladbroke Grove, Westbourne Park **Bus:** 7, 23, 28, 31, 52, 70, 295, 302 **Payment:** cash, cheque

Golborne Fisheries' Mauritian owner George Ng introduced the exotic fish of his native shores to Golborne Road and has now opened a restaurant directly opposite the shop. Impressively, Ng bypasses Billingsgate and sources his supply directly from abroad. Crayfish comes from Cuba and Mozambique, while *capitaine blanc* is flown over from Mauritius. Rarer fish such as *rascasse* – intrinsic to *bouillabaisse* – weaver and parrot fish are also regularly on offer. Jamie Oliver and Anthony Worrall Thompson are among the celebrity chefs who can be spotted browsing among the langoustines, lobster tails, tiger prawns and yellow grouper. Astutely, Ng caters for his cosmopolitan clientele: he says

the conger eel, octopus and black sabre fish are favoured by the Portuguese; squid and hake by the Spanish; and the exotics such as red snapper, king fish and dolphin fish are preferred by the Afro-Caribbean community. For Brits with more traditional tastes, there are also whole salmon and tuna sliced to order, monkfish, mussels, oysters, scallops, live spider crabs and top-quality cod – the last two supplied directly by fishermen in Plymouth.

THE GRAIN SHOP
269A Portobello Road,
London W11 1LR
Tel: 020 7229 5571
Open: Mon-Sat 9.30am-6pm, Sun 10am-4.30pm **Closed:** 25, 26 Dec., 1 Jan. **Tube:** Notting Hill Gate, Ladbroke Grove **Bus:** 7, 23, 28, 52, 70, 295 **Payment:** cash, cheque, Amex, Delta, Maestro, MasterCard, Visa **Food-to-go**

Bakery
Organic
Special Diet

People come to this small shop from miles around to buy their bread, which, like all the food on offer here, is baked on the premises. Only organic flour is used, and the loaves come in yeast-free, wheat-free and sugar-free varieties. Favourites include the large sourdough loaf, the rice bread made with organic wholemeal flour peppered with brown rice, and the sunflower seed bread, which is so moist it has the texture and flavour of nutty cake. There are also wheat- and yeast-free rye

Portobello Road Market

Open: Mon, Tues, Wed, Fri, Sat 8am-6.30pm, Thurs 8am-1pm **Closed:** Sun **Tube:** Notting Hill Gate, Ladbroke Grove **Bus:** 7, 12, 23, 27, 28, 31, 52, 70, 94, 328

This is perhaps the most eclectic London market of them all and really does deserve a whole day of a visit. (In fact, you really need two days to see and absorb everything.) At the Notting Hill Gate end, antique stalls, shops and indoor markets sell an amazing variety of goods, from cigarette cards and old tins and boxes to silver jugs and grandfather clocks. At the more northerly, seedier end, there are many supposed second-hand stalls – but a lot of the stock, mainly clothes, looks more fourth or fifth hand. In between, there are craft and bric-à-brac markets – many young designers showcase their work here – and the food market. The food stalls stretch roughly from Colville Terrace to Lancaster Road, lining one side of the road. They operate to a lesser extent during the week, supplying fairly ordinary but surprisingly cheap fruit and vegetables to the locals, but come into their own on a Saturday, when the place is packed. That's when the fast-food sellers appear. They offer Thai noodles and Jamaican patties – the latter a reminder of the Afro-Caribbean flavour of the area, which is exemplified by the Notting Hill Carnival, held here yearly at the end of August. There are good fish, bread and meat stalls, and you can also find glorious cut flowers. On Thursdays under the Westway, from 11am-6pm, there's a small organic market, with good vegetables, bread, meats, dried fruit and nuts. Don't miss The Spice Shop (page 106) and Books for Cooks (page 98), just round the corner in Blenheim Crescent.

sourdough, olive and rosemary, and honey-sweetened corn loaves. Teatime treats include vegan sugar-free date and lemon slices and vegan wheat-free sesame and gluten-free flapjacks. The takeaway dishes are also a major attraction. Every day, you'll find a daily range of 17 hot dishes and five to eight salads. Prices start at £2.50 for a small container holding three choices and rise to £3.80 and £4.95 for a larger container holding as many choices as you like.

Delicatessen
Traiteur

THE GROCER ON ELGIN
6 Elgin Crescent,
London W11 2HX
Tel: 020 7221 3844

Branch: see Soho, page 52

Butcher
Game dealer
Organic
Free range
Delicatessen

★ KINGSLAND – THE EDWARDIAN BUTCHERS
140 Portobello Road,
London W11 2DZ
Tel/Fax: 020 7727 6067
Open: Mon-Sat 8.30am-5.30pm
Closed: Sun, Bank holidays **Tube:** Notting Hill Gate, Ladbroke Grove **Bus:** 23, 52, 70 **Payment:** cash, cheque, Amex, Delta, Maestro, MasterCard, Visa
Free local delivery, accounts available

Truly a family business, Kingsland styles itself as an Edwardian butcher with old-fashioned values and friendly, personal service. It offers a wide choice of free-range, organic and speciality meats: the pork is supplied from rare breeds such as Gloucester Old Spot, Middle White and British Saddleback, while the beef is from Aberdeen Angus, Longhorn and Ayrshire grass-fed cattle. Indeed, Kingsland is London's only accredited Rare Breeds Survival Trust retail outlet. The sausages are all handmade and come in interesting combinations such as apricot and garlic, merguez, wild boar and apple, and sun-dried tomato with herbs and spices. Dressed cuts such as crown roast and saddle of lamb are prepared on request. In summer, you'll find marinated meats for barbecues, casseroles and kebabs. In season, game might range from English partridge, teal, woodcock and widgeon to guinea fowl, grouse, mallard, pheasant, pigeon and even peacock. Exotica available to order includes the likes of crocodile and locusts. The deli counter offers assorted salume, cold meats, free-range and quail eggs, pâtés and cheeses, plus proprietor Haydn Field's excellent home-made pies. Lining the shelves are Mrs Bridges' chutneys, mustards, lime and lemon curds, marmalades and conserves; a variety of country-style stuffings; and jars of sauces including cranberry with port and pickle.

Halal
Moroccan
Grocer
Greengrocer
Delicatessen

★ LE MAROC

94 Golborne Road,
London W10 5PS
Tel. 020 8968 9783
Open: Mon-Sat 9am-8pm
Closed: Sun, Bank holidays **Tube:** Ladbroke Grove, Westbourne Park **Bus:** 7, 23, 28, 31, 52, 70, 295, 302 **Payment:** cash, cheque

Once inside this shop, you are instantly transported to Morocco. A colourful display of glazed earthenware tagine pots, couscous steamers, teapots, and ornate wall plates greets the eye. It's the food, though, that draws the local, very cosmopolitan clientele. The halal meat counter sells home-made kofte, spicy merguez sausages, Moroccan salami and marinated cubes of meat and chicken with spices and herbs, as well as lamb chops, legs and shoulders. From the cold cabinet, try the different kinds of feta. Occupying central stage are huge wooden bowls of olives, ranging from small, pitted white olives for tagines to Greek Kalamata. Alongside is a big pot of ghee, whole preserved lemons, dried fruit and delicious *shabaki* (fennel and spice pastry twirls soaked in honey and dipped in sesame seeds). Open wooden boxes offer loose fine and medium couscous, three grades of semolina, pulses, beans, grains, dried raisins, sultanas and apricots. The shelves are laden with a fine selection of tea including loose gunpowder, tins

of *halva*, black and green olives, extra virgin olive oils, honeys, packets of almonds and Tunisian dates on the vine. Just outside, you'll find unleavened bread and fresh herbs.

LE MARRAKECH

64 Golborne Road,
London W10 5PS
Tel: 020 8964 8307
Open: Mon-Sat 9am-7.30pm
Closed: Sun, Bank holidays
Tube: Westbourne Park,
Ladbroke Grove **Bus:** 7, 23, 28, 31, 52, 295 **Payment:** cash, cheque, MasterCard, Visa
Catering

Mohammed Benariba hails from Marrakech, so all of the goods here have a Moroccan slant. You'll find a wide variety of olives, olive oils, pickles, pungent preserved lemons, home-made harissa and a plethora of Middle Eastern ingredients ranging from couscous to *ful medames* beans in tins. Baklava, cakes and Moroccan sweets are available during Ramadan. Benariba also sells tagines, *couscousières* and other decorative dishes, which are essential for recreating that authentic, Moroccan look at home.

L'ETOILE DE SOUS

79 Golborne Road,
London W10 5NL
Tel: 020 8960 9769
Open: Mon-Sat 8am-6pm
Closed: Sun, Bank holidays

Moroccan
Delicatessen
Grocer
Greengrocer

North African
Pâtisserie

Tube: Ladbroke Grove, Westbourne Park **Bus:** 7, 23, 28, 31, 52, 70, 295, 302 **Payment:** cash, cheque

This irresistible North African and French pâtisserie boasts a huge variety of pastries made on the premises. Moroccan and Tunisian specialities include nutty fruited rusks, coconut macaroons and shortcrust crescents, squares, boats and oblongs – with almond, hazelnut, rosewater, and clove and date fillings – all dusted in icing sugar and piled high on huge baking trays in the window. There is a wonderful assortment of millefeuille baklava soaked in honey and stuffed with pistachios or almonds. During Ramadan, be sure to try the cinnamon and fennel spiced honey and sesame twirls and the crisp, honeyed pastries. Notable bread includes sesame-sprinkled long white loaves, which are also available in crescents, and flat brown and white loaves scored with a cross. Another North African speciality is a large, flat unleavened bread, doughy in texture, which can accompany savoury dishes or be spread with cheese or jam.

Portuguese Delicatessen

★ LISBOA DELICATESSEN
54 Golborne Road,
London W10 5NR
Tel: 020 8969 1586
Fax: 020 8964 1976
Open: Mon-Sat 9.30am-7.30pm, Sun 10am-1pm **Closed:** Bank holidays, 25, 26 Dec., 1 Jan.
Tube: Ladbroke Grove, Westbourne Park **Bus:** 7, 23, 28, 31, 52, 70, 295, 302 **Payment:** cash, Delta, Maestro, MasterCard, Visa

London's largest, best and most friendly Portuguese deli sits across the street from its pâtisserie sister and is 'like having Portugal at home', say its customers. The shelves are crammed full with all sorts of groceries, from virgin and extra virgin olive oils, beans, pulses, pasta, rice, rusks, baby foods, powdered *pudim* mixes, dried figs, nuts, raisins, jams (including tomato and quince) and crystallized fruit to tins of sardines, mussels, anchovies, baby eels and pickled vegetables. Herbs and spice mixtures include hot piri-piri. Huge sides of *bacalhau* – dried salt cod – are piled high, ready for cutting to order, along with pigs' trotters, noses and ears, which are typically used to make a *feijoada* or bean stew. The deli counter stocks cured meats and salamis, *morcela*

Olive oil, wine and friendship, the older the better.

Portuguese proverb

blood sausage, smoked pork ribs, mild Portuguese *chouriço* and *presunto* smoked ham, as well as an impressive variety of cheeses – *cabra*, manchego, creamy *queijo alavao* and pungent, nutty *queijo Azores*. There are also loose black, green, Kalamata and garlic herbed olives. Christmas treats include packets of muscatel raisins, sugar or chocolate coated almonds, and honey and spice corn cookies.

Branches: see Camden, page 115, Fulham, page 84

Portuguese
Pâtisserie

LISBOA PÂTISSERIE

57 Golborne Road,
London W10 5NR
Tel: 020 8968 5242
Fax: 020 8964 1976
Open: Mon-Sun 8am-7.30pm
Closed: 25, 26 Dec., 1 Jan., Bank holidays **Tube:** Ladbroke Grove, Westbourne Park **Bus:** 7, 23, 28, 31, 52, 70, 295, 302 **Payment:** cash, Delta, Maestro, MasterCard, Visa
Delivery (for large orders)

This Portuguese bakery is always crowded. Most people come to buy pastries and cakes, all of which are home-made, and stay to sample them over a cup of really excellent Sical coffee. Regulars adore the *pasteis de bacalhau* (salt-cod fish cakes) and *pasteis de nata*. The cinnamon-spiced *travesseiro* or pillow cake, which is filled with pumpkin, and *queijada de Sintra*, an orangey cream cheese

cake, are equally irresistible. The shop also sells a wide range of savoury, meat-filled pastries.

MR CHRISTIAN'S

11 Elgin Crescent,
London W11 2JA
Tel: 020 7229 0501
Fax: 020 7727 6980
Website: www.jeroboams.co.uk
Open: Mon-Fri 6am-7pm, Sat 6am-6.30pm, Sun 7.30am-5pm
Closed: 25, 26 Dec., 1 Jan, Notting Hill carnival in August
Tube: Notting Hill Gate, Ladbroke Grove **Bus:** 23, 52, 70
Payment: cash, cheque, Amex, Delta, Maestro, MasterCard, Visa
Catering, food-to-go

Once owned by the famous New Zealand cookery writer and television broadcaster, Glynn Christian, this deli has become a Notting Hill institution. It's renowned for the knowledgable, efficient and friendly service of managers Matt Ansons and Ben Harrou and their staff. Shelves and tables groan with marvellous bread, such as & Clarke's fig and fennel, rosemary and raisin, and olive and sun-dried tomato loaves (page 92). The caramelized garlic French farmhouse loaf from Baker & Spice (page 20) invariably

Delicatessen
Bakery

Once owned by the famous New

Le Pont de la Tour Foodstore

Bermondsey – *see page 154*

Taj Stores

Shoreditch – *see page 69*

Villandry

Fitzrovia – *see page 32*

Lina Stores

Soho – *see page 53*

> Eating ethically is all about knowing where your food comes from, and how it has been produced. Londoners are the trailblazers for ethical eating… The trend has shifted from being vegetarian in the Eighties, buying organic in the Nineties to well being today.

Genevieve Fox, food writer

sells out. Just as enticing are the shop's almond croissants, own-made flapjacks and chocolate brownies. Mr Christian's cabinets are abundantly stocked with huge bowls of olives, 25 types of salume, home-made pâtés and pesto – try rocket or walnut – and some 90 varieties of carefully chosen cheeses from Britain and Europe. Extra boxes of chocolates and truffles are ordered for special occasions, while at Christmas, Italian *panettone* and *pandoro* sway from the ceiling. In summer, the speciality olive oils and vinegars, including mouth-watering blood-orange vinegar (ideal for salad dressing) and black fig vinegar, are extremely popular. Don't leave without seeking out the shop's extensive conserves, chutneys, relishes, mustards, jellies, pasta sauces and own-brand lime, lemon and banoffee curds.

PORTOBELLO WHOLEFOODS

266 Portobello Road,
London W10 5TY
Tel: 020 8968 9133
Fax: 020 8960 1840
Open: Mon-Sat 9.30am-6pm,
Sun 11am-5pm **Closed:** 25, 26
Dec., 1 Jan., Notting Hill
carnival in August **Tube:** Notting
Hill Gate, Ladbroke Grove **Bus:**
7, 23, 28, 52, 70 **Payment:** cash,
cheque, Delta, MasterCard,
Maestro, Solo, Visa

The key to Portobello Wholefoods' interesting, large range of vegetarian and health food products lies in its former ownership by Neal's Yard Bakery, from where its bread still comes. (The organic sunflower and small organic three-seed loaves are among the best-sellers.) Now independent, quality and diversity continue to be maintained here, and the shelves are stacked with an impressive selection of organic and wholefood goodies,

Wholefoods
Organic
Special diet

including a range for those on vegan, macrobiotic and detox diets. Also on offer are pure fruit spreads and honey from around the world, plus culinary and medicinal herbs and spices. At Christmas, be sure to try the rich, gluten-free plum pudding, the GM-free, vegan Christmas cake and the Ultimate Organic Christmas Cake, which is also GM-free and soaked in organic brandy.

Herbs
Spices
Organic

★ THE SPICE SHOP

1 Blenheim Crescent,
London W11 2EE
Tel: 020 7221 4448
Inquiries tel: 020 7221 4960
Website: www.thespiceshop.co.uk
Open: Mon-Sat 9am-6pm, Sun 11am-4pm **Closed:** occasional Bank holidays **Tube:** Ladbroke Grove **Bus:** 7, 23, 52, 70
Payment: cash, cheque, Delta,Maestro, MasterCard, Visa
Catalogue, mail order

From *agar agar* to *zahtar* via *epazote*, laos powder and *sumach*, this tiny shop specializes in flavourings from all over the globe. Proprietor Birgit Erath goes to great lengths to source unusual ingredients and supports small peasant farmers, whose produce she markets exclusively. In addition to the range of herbs and spices, Erath also stocks Japanese, Thai and other Oriental ingredients; flavoured salts, curry mixes, argon oil, *penja* peppercorns and dried

wild mushrooms; plus fresh ingredients including kaffir lime and curry leaves, lemongrass, galangal, root ginger, tomatillos and new garlic. In late August, the Mexican chillies (*cascabel, poblano, habanero* etc.) arrive. French dressings, flavoured olive oils and high-quality mustards can also be found here, as well as specialized kitchen utensils such as Chinese wooden ginger graters, nutmeg graters and pepper grinders.

★ TAVOLA

155 Westbourne Grove,
LondonW11 2RS
Tel: 020 7229 0571
Fax: 020 7792 3283
Open: Mon–Fri 10am–7.30pm, Sat 9.30am–5pm **Closed:** Sun
Tube: Bayswater, Royal Oak
Bus: 7, 23, 27, 36, 70
Payment: cash, cheque, Amex, Delta, MasterCard, Maestro, Visa
Food-to-go, picnic hampers

Italian
Delicatessen

Every neighbourhood should have a deli/*traiteur* like this one. Run by top chef Alastair Little and his wife, Sharon, Tavola's emphasis is on top-quality, seasonal foods, often with an Italian inflection. Unless a product is 'gobsmackingly tasty', the Littles will neither cook with it nor stock it, according to Sharon. 'We don't go for extraneous decoration – just simple, good food without any titivating fluff,' she says. The principal line is the food-to-go, which is prepared daily by Alastair and his staff in the adjoining kitchen. A rustic, central table groans with mouth-wateringly tasty dishes including, on our visit, broad beans with chilli, lemon and parsley; new season King Edward potatoes with garlic; and roast breast of free-range, corn-fed chicken in harissa marinade. In the window, brownies made with Valrhona chocolate, New York-style cheesecake and white chocolate mousse, drizzled with strawberry and Balsamic sauce, are among the temptations. Tavola is also well-stocked with products that, collectively, would form anyone's dream store cupboard. 'We went through our own pantry and took a look at what we use and what we love,' explains Sharon. You'll find Machiavelli cured meats, Neal's Yard cheeses (page 31), bread from Exeter Street Bakery, artisanal pasta from Puglia, an exclusive line of olive oil – plus jars of fresh herbs and spices, and baskets of vegetables that are delivered twice a day. You could easily blow your weekly food budget here in one visit. But, as Sharon quite rightly puts it: 'Food is something you really shouldn't stint on.'

THE TEA AND COFFEE PLANT

180 Portobello Road, London W11 2EB
Tel/Fax: 020 7221 8137
Mail-order tel: 020 7655 4575
Website: www.coffee.uk.com
Open: Mon-Sat 8am-8.30pm, Sun 9am-5pm **Closed:** Bank holidays **Tube:** Ladbroke Grove **Bus:** 23, 52, 70 **Payment:** cash, cheque, Delta, Maestro, MasterCard, Visa
Mail order

Coffee
Tea

The smell is as wonderful as the choice at this shop, which specializes in organic, fair-trade coffee. The beans are all roasted at the shop's own roastery on Brick Lane and are ground right in front of you. The light roasts produce a creamy, slightly acidic taste; the medium are fairly floral; and the dark pack a definite punch. On the right, as you enter the shop, you'll find traditional, fruit and medicinal

❝ I prefer to go to small shops for my spices, as they tend to be better produced, sourced and stored. ❞

Jamie Oliver

tea, which The Tea and Coffee Plant blends itself; confectionary including the popular chocolate gingers, chocolate almond bars and cooking chocolate; and high-quality coffee-making equipment. At the end of the shop is the bean counter. Here, you can buy the shop's best-selling Italian roast, organic, fair-trade Mexican and house-blend coffee – or treat yourself to a cappuccino and freshly baked croissant.

Delicatessen
Bakery

TOM'S DELI
226 Westbourne Grove, London W11 2RH
Tel: 020 7221 8818
Fax: 020 7221 7717
Open: Mon-Sat 8am-6pm, Sun and Bank holidays 9am-4pm
Closed: Notting Hill carnival in August **Tube:** Notting Hill Gate, Wesbourne Park **Bus:** 7, 23, 27, 28, 31, 52, 328 **Payment:** cash, cheque, Delta, Electron, Maestro, MasterCard, Solo, Visa
Catering, delivery, food-to-go

Temptation strikes as soon as you step into this shop, which is owned by Sir Terence Conran's son, Tom. Near the entrance, a cold cabinet is stuffed with a selection of sweets such as home-made fruit crumble and bread and butter pudding. Opposite, you'll find a range of bread, croissants and sandwiches. The rest of the deli is a haven of hidden delights, including hard-to-find Seresin

and Planeta olive oils, Jules & Sharpie's condiments, Betty Crocker cake mixes and frostings, Irish smoked salmon, Parma ham, olives, marinated vegetables, pickles, seafood, antipasti and a selection of fine wines from New Zealand, Italy, France and Portugal. The cheeses are sourced primarily from Spanish and English suppliers and include the likes of manchego; Sabor de España, Waterloo and Ribblesdale goat's cheeses; and Quickes mature cheddar. Beef lasagne, *gnocchi di patate*, spicy tomato and mushroom pasta sauces, prepared salads and several different pestos are among the huge variety of appetising foods-to-go. Upstairs is the deli's cosy café, which is popular with celebrities including comedian Dave Allen and supermodel Kate Moss.

Shepherd's Bush

BUSH GARDEN CAFÉ & FOOD STORE
59–61 Goldhawk Road, London W12 8EG
Tel: 020 8743 6372
Open: Mon-Sat 8am-5.30pm
Closed: Sun **Tube:** Goldhawk Road, Shepherd's Bush **Bus:** 72, 94, 220, 237, 283, 295
Payment: cash, Amex, Delta, Maestro, MasterCard, Visa
Food-to-go

Organic
Food Hall

Mairead Fanning's goal when she launched this cosy organic food hall/eatery in 2004 was to provide a 'nicer alternative' to the plentiful fast-food restaurants along Goldhawk Road. She's clearly filled a void, because the Bush Garden Café has become a magnet for local mums and office workers. They come partly for the in-house kitchen's delicious juices, smoothies, soups, salads and sandwiches – the ginger spice drink and chicken, pumpkin and jalapeño pepper soup sounded particularly enticing on our visit – but also for the well-stocked food hall. Its shelves are laden with organic foods of every description. You'll find a selection of ready meals, wines, olive oils, pasta sauces, dairy products, tea, coffee, biscuits, cereals and baby foods. But just when your basket is full and you're starting to feel virtuous, you'll notice the irresistibly plump packets of Oreo cookies and the large glass jar full of Chupa Chups lollipops. 'I'm a mum myself and I wanted to open a café that appeals to parents and their children,' Fanning notes.

Middle
Eastern
Halal
Grocer
Greengrocer

DAMAS GATE

81-85 Uxbridge Road,
London W12 7NR
Tel: 020 8743 5116,
020 8723 8428
Fax: 020 8749 0235
Open: Mon-Sun 9am-9pm
Tube: Shepherd's Bush **Bus:** 207,
260, 283 **Payment:** cash, cheque,
Amex, Delta, Maestro,
MasterCard, Visa
Catering, food-to-go

This attractive delicatessen is a treat for the eye, with its colourful display of exotic fruit and vegetables on the pavement, and its array of Lebanese pastries inside. You'll also find a good range of bread, from pitta to large flat bread. There is a halal butcher's counter with a fair selection of fresh meats, and the cheese section offers Middle Eastern cheeses, as well as Bulgarian feta. The deli counter has a breathtaking display of attractively packaged Middle Eastern food-to-go, including houmous, tabouleh, spring rolls, samosas, falafel, *ful medames* and *mohallabia*. The staff is welcoming and always more than willing to help.

JOHN & SONS

103 Uxbridge Road,
London W12 8NL
Tel: 020 8743 9224
Open: Mon-Fri 8am-7pm, Sat
8.30am-6pm **Closed:** Sun, Bank
holidays **Tube:** Shepherd's Bush
(Metropolitan line) **Payment:**
cash, cheque, Amex, Delta,
Maestro, MasterCard, Visa

This small, characterful delicatessen is run by the Banian brothers and stocks a wide range of products from Serbia, Croatia, Bulgaria and Poland. You'll also find risotto rice, Parma ham, dried mushrooms and cheeses from Italy, and a huge range of pickles, including pickled

Eastern
European
Delicatessen

cabbage from Slovenia – an in-house speciality. The drink selection includes top-quality Russian vodka, Slovenian wine and Albanian cognac.

Thai
Grocer
Greengrocer

SRI THAI
56 Shepherds Bush Road,
London W6 7PH
Tel/Fax: 020 7602 0621
Open: Mon-Sun 9.30am-7pm
Tube: Hammersmith, Shepherd's
Bush **Bus:** 72, 220, 295, 283
Payment: cash, cheque
Food-to-go

This small grocery shop, launched by Sombat and Pascharin Thepprasits in 1986, specializes in Thai food and has a good range of fresh vegetables and herbs, which are flown in from Thailand every Tuesday. You can usually find Thai aubergines, kai lan, coconuts and a wonderful range of chillies and fresh fruit, including rambutans. Most of the fruit and veg is seasonal, but as the Thai growing season is so long, it tends to be available for most of the year. The grocery side of the shop stocks 10 different kinds of fresh curry pastes, along with a selection of tinned pastes, dried noodles of every variety, fragrant and glutinous rice, potato rice, glutinous rice and tapioca flours, and a delicious range of Thai dressings and sauces. There is also a large variety of frozen fish. Fresh noodles and egg noodles are available every Wednesday, barbecue pork is made fresh each Saturday and sticky rice with banana and jam wrapped in banana leaf (the shop's speciality) is prepared daily. Sri Thai's vegetable dumplings, spring rolls, fish cakes and fresh ready meals are also extremely popular.

YASAR HALIM
182 Uxbridge Road,
London W12 7JP
Tel: 020 8740 9477

Main shop: see Harringay,
page 140

Turkish
Bakery
Pâtisserie
Greengrocer
Grocer

Shepherd's Bush Market

Open: Mon-Wed, Fri, Sat 9am-5pm, Thurs 9am-1pm **Closed:** Sun **Tube:** Shepherd's Bush (Hammersmith and City Line), Goldhawk Road **Bus:** 23, 49, 52, 70, 94, 95, 207, 220, 237, 260, 283, 295

This market stretches from Shepherd's Bush to Goldhawk Road tube stations, running in a narrow arc alongside the railway viaduct, and into the arches beneath. Permanent shops occupy the arches, stalls the middle, and the other side of the narrow street is crammed with lock-up shacks. It is less a food market than a general household needs market, but with an international flavour that is enticing. There are stalls selling shoes, pots and pans, saris, household linens, hats fit for a Royal garden party, greetings cards, sweets, hair jewellery, wigs, candles and suitcases. A couple of conventional fruit and vegetable stalls at each end of the market offer good scoops and bags of selected produce for £1. In the middle of the market, there is a stall with probably the most varied Afro-Caribbean/Asian fruit and vegetables outside Brixton – including *dasheen*, *chowchow* (or *chayote*), okra, several types of sweet potato and fat, thin and long beans. There are a couple of good fishmongers, one of which, W. H. Roe, sells a huge variety of tropical fish, including yellow croakers, trevally, jacks and pomfret. Butchers cater for the special tastes of their Asian, Caribbean and Irish customers, too, offering halal meat and chickens, various cuts of goat (one of which is especially for curry), tripe, tongue and singed cows' feet. Be sure to try some falafel or a traditional British fry-up at one of the several nearby cafés.

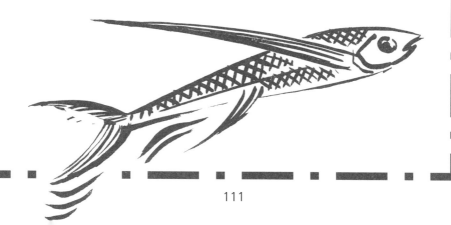

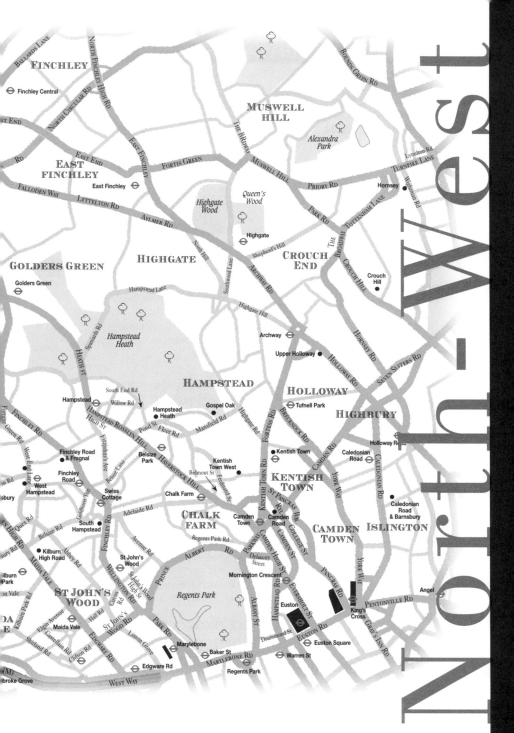

FINCHLEY

⊖ Finchley Central

ST END

NORTH CIRCULAR RD

NORTH FINCHLEY HIGH RD

BALLARD'S LANE

MUSWELL
HILL

BOUNDS GREEN RD

Alexandra
Park

RD

EAST END

EAST
FINCHLEY

FALLODEN WAY

East Finchley ⊖

LYTTELTON RD

EAST FINCHLEY

FORTIS GREEN

MUSWELL HILL

THE BROADWAY

PRIORY RD

PARK RD

Hornsey

TOTTENHAM LANE

TURNPIKE LANE

Lyttelton Rd

Wightman Rd

Queen's
Wood

GOLDERS GREEN

Golders Green ●

HIGHGATE

AYLMER RD

Highgate
Wood

North Hill

Highgate
⊖

Shepherd's Hill

CROUCH
END

THE BROADWAY

CROUCH HILL

Crouch
Hill
●

HORNSEY RD

SEVEN SISTERS RD

Hampstead Lane

Southwood Lane

ARCHWAY RD

Highgate Hill

Archway
⊖

Upper Holloway ●

HOLLOWAY RD

Hampstead
Heath

Spaniard's Rd

HEATH ST

HAMPSTEAD

HOLLOWAY

HIGHBURY

Holloway Road
⊖

South End Rd

Hampstead ● Willow Rd

FINCHLEY RD

Fortune Green Rd

West End Lane

Hampstead
● Heath

Gospel Oak
●

Tufnell Park
⊖

HAMPSTEAD
HIGH ST

ROSSLIN HILL

Pond St

Fleet Rd

Mansfield Rd

Highgate Rd

FORTESS RD

BRECKNOCK RD

Fitzjohn's Ave

Belsize Lane

Finchley Road
& Frognal
●

Belsize
Park
⊖

HAVERSTOCK HILL

Kentish Town West
⊖

Kentish Town ●
⊖

KENTISH TOWN RD

Caledonian
Road
⊖

CALEDONIAN RD

Holloway Road
⊖

En Rd

Finchley
Road
⊖

West
Hampstead
⊖

Swiss
Cottage
⊖

Chalk Farm
⊖

Belmont St

Ferdinand St

KENTISH
TOWN

CAMDEN HIGH ST

CAMDEN ST

YORK WAY

Caledonian
Road
& Barnsbury
●

sbury

Goldhurst Terr

Adelaide Rd

South ●
Hampstead

FINCHLEY RD

CHALK
FARM

Camden
Town
⊖

Camden
Road
⊖

St Pancras Way

COLLEGE ST

CAMDEN
TOWN

ISLINGTON

N Quex Rd

Belsize Rd

Avenue Rd

Regents Park Rd

Delancey
Street

Mornington Crescent
⊖

PARKWAY

CAMDEN HIGH ST

PANCRAS RD

YORK WAY

Angel

High Rd

Kilburn ●
High Road

St John's
Wood
⊖

ALBERT RD

Euston
⊖

King's
Cross
⊖

PENTONVILLE RD

GRAY'S INN RD

bury Rd

MAIDA VALE

Abbey Rd

WELLINGTON RD

PRINCE ALBERT RD

Regents Park

Euston ⊖

Euston Square
⊖

EUSTON RD

lburn
Park

on Vale

ST JOHN'S
WOOD

Elgin Avenue

Maida Vale
⊖

Kilburn Park Rd

Hall Rd

ST JOHN'S
WOOD RD

Circus

St John's Wood High St

PARK RD

LISSON GROVE

Drummond St

Marylebone
⊖

Baker St
⊖

Warren St
⊖

DA
E

Shirland Rd

Castellain Rd

Clifton Rd

EDGWARE RD

Edgware Rd
⊖

MARYLEBONE RD

Regents Park
⊖

(M)
broke Grove

WEST WAY

Belsize Park

Delicatessen

BELSIZE VILLAGE DELICATESSEN

39 Belsize Lane,
London NW3 5AS
Tel: 020 7794 4258
Open: Mon-Fri 8.30am-7pm, Sat
8.30am-6pm, Sun, Bank
holidays 9am-2pm **Tube:** Swiss
Cottage **Bus:** 13, 31, 46, 82, 113,
268 **Mainline station:** South
Hampstead **Payment:** cash,
cheque, Delta, Maestro,
MasterCard, Visa
Food-to-go

This busy, well-stocked deli has
an interesting and eclectic range
of goods. Its top notch range of
sausages includes Portuguese
chouriço, frankfurters, Toulouse
sausages and *boudins blanc et
noirs*, plus Polish, Italian and
French varieties. You'll also find
delicious herrings, artichokes,
aubergines in oil, olives, and
lentil, couscous and bean salads.
The prepared food-to-go varies,
but usually includes *pissaladière*,
boeuf bourguignon, steak and
kidney pie, chicken *chasseur*,
shepherd's pie, canelloni, lasagne
and stuffed aubergines. An
excellent cheese counter offers
the likes of Brie de Meaux, real
crottins de chèvre and *Reblochon
fermière*. The strong baked
goods section is crammed
with desserts such as
pecan pie, coconut
tart and chocolate
fudge cake, as well
as a wide range of
fresh bread supplied

by specialist Italian, German,
Ukrainian, Italian and Greek
bakers. The shop also has a good
range of hams, pâtés and terrines
and even offers its own fresh foie
gras at Christmas.

THE DELICATESSEN SHOP

Delicatessen

23 South End Road,
London NW3 2PT
Tel: 020 7435 7315
Open: Mon-Fri 9.30am-7pm, Sat
9am-6pm **Closed:** Sun, Bank
holidays **Tube:** Belsize Park **Bus:**
24, 168 **Mainline station:**
Hampstead Heath **Payment:**
cash, cheque, Delta, Maestro,
Mastercard (£10 minimum),
Visa (£10 minimum)
Food-to-go

Situated across the street from
the mainline station, this long,
narrow shop is crammed with
mouth-watering items. It sells a
good range of cheeses,
including ewe's milk manchego
and *graviera* goat's cheese from
Crete, plus a number of fresh
pasta, *funghetto*, clam and pesto
sauces, and a selection of
salume and Italian sausages.
You'll also find bread and
cakes, and prepared dishes such
as lentil burgers and fish cakes.
The service is unfailingly helpful
and friendly.

LE PROVENÇAL

Delicatessen

167 Haverstock Hill,
London NW3 4QT
Tel: 020 7586 2574
Open: Mon-Fri 9.30am-8pm, Sat
9.30am-7pm, Sun 9.30am-3pm
Closed: Bank holidays **Tube:**

Belsize Park **Bus:** 168, C11, C12 **Payment:** cash, cheque, Maestro (over £10) MasterCard, Visa

This well-established deli has been in business for more than 30 years and is a favourite with locals. The produce is mainly French, Italian and Spanish, but the shop also has a good selection of British cheeses. Maxim's de Paris and Fresh French Pâtisserie supply the delicious chocolates and cakes, respectively, while the bread come from respected bakers Exeter Street Bakery and Baker & Spice (page 20). The aforementioned cheeses – there are about 120 varieties – are supplied by Neal's Yard Dairy (page 31) and La Fromagerie (page 141). You'll also find fresh pasta sourced directly from Tuscany; Spanish meats, including tasty Iberico ham, from Brindisa; antipasti including sun-dried tomatoes, aubergines in oil, and dips and salads; plus home-cooked food-to-go including pasta, lasagna, cannelloni and moussaka. Store-cupboard items include a good range of jams, preserves, marmalades and chutneys, plus some excellent French and Italian wines.

Camden

CAMDEN COFFEE STORES

Coffee

11 Delancey Street,
London NW1 7NL
Tel: 020 7387 4080
Open: Mon-Wed, Fri-Sat 9.30am-5.30pm, Thurs 9.30am-2.30pm **Closed:** Sun, Bank holidays **Tube:** Camden Town, Mornington Crescent **Bus:** C2, 24, 27, 29, 31, 134, 135, 168, 214, 253, 274 **Payment:** cash

This tiny shop perfumes the entire street with the enticing aroma of roasting coffee beans. Hessian sacks of pale, unroasted beans line the walls; by the counter are bread containers full of their glossy, dark brown, roasted equivalents – up to 10 different varieties. Roasting is done on the premises, and the beans can be roasted, ground and/or blended to individual specifications.

★ FRESH & WILD

Food Hall
Organic

49 Parkway,
London NW1 7PN
Tel: 020 7428 7575

Main shop and branches: see Notting Hill, page 97

★ LISBOA DELICATESSEN

Portuguese
Delicatessen

4, Plender Street,
London NW1 0JT
Tel: 020 7387 1782

Main shop: see Notting Hill, page 103

Chalk Farm

Sausages

AUSTRIAN SAUSAGE CENTRE

10A Belmont Street,
London NW1 8HH
Tel: 020 7267 3601
Fax: 020 7482 4965
Open: Mon-Fri 7am-5pm, Sat
7am-1pm **Closed:** Sun, Bank
holidays **Tube:** Chalk Farm **Bus:**
24, 27, 31, 168 **Payment:** cash

This shop may look a bit basic,
but that's because it is a
manufacturing outlet first and
foremost. There's a cooler
cabinet and little else here, but
you'll find good-quality cooked
meats and sausages – many of
which are made to recipes from
Austria and other points East.
Everything is prepared on
the premises and is sold at
factory prices.

Gelateria

MARINE ICES

8 Haverstock Hill,
London NW3 2BL
Tel: 020 7482 9003
Open: Mon-Fri 8am-10am, Sat
and Sun 9am-10pm
Tube: Chalk Farm **Bus:** C11, 24,
31, 168 **Mainline Station:**
Kentish Town West
Payment: cash, cheque, Delta,
Maestro, MasterCard, Visa

Many locals, and their parents,
will remember coming to this
authentic Italian gelateria for
childhood treats. Opened in
1931, and now run by the
original owner's grandsons
Dante, Gaetano and Gino

Mansi, it offers nearly 30
flavours of fresh fruit sorbet
and dairy ice cream. All –
including the scrumptious
raspberry, amarena cherry,
mint, hazelnut and pistachio
– are made on site, and most
can be taken away in very
reasonably priced half-litre
and four-litre tubs.

MOTA'S BAKERY

British
Polish
Bakery

8 Ferdinand Street,
London NW1 8ER
Tel: 020 7284 4644
Open: Mon-Fri 8am-5pm, Sat
and Sun 11am-5pm **Closed:**
Bank holidays **Tube:** Chalk
Farm **Bus:** 24, 27, 31, 46, 168
Payment: cash, cheque
Catering, food-to-go

This tiny corner shop
advertises sandwiches, but
there is much more on offer,
including healthy dishes on
hot plates, organic pizzas and
vegetarian chow mein. There
are a few groceries, but the
traditional English and Polish
bread, in particular a four-
seed wholemeal loaf that is
packed with flavour, is the
star of the show.

Colindale

ORIENTAL CITY

South-East
Asian
Food Hall

399 Edgware Road,
London NW9 0JJ
Tel: 020 8205 8220
Fax: 020 8200 0848
Open: Mon-Sat 10am-9pm,
Sun 12pm-6pm **Tube:**
Colindale **Bus:** 32, 142

Payment: cash, cheque, Maestro, MasterCard, Solo, Visa
Food-to-go

This large, no-frills shopping centre is dedicated to the food and culture of the Far East. There are plenty of Korean, Chinese, Thai, Indonesian and Malaysian specialities, although Japanese food predominates. Exotic fruit and veg are flown in from Asia twice a week and include everything from Chinese pears, custard apples, durian and white and green mooli, to pak choy, ong choy, kai choy, string beans, white aubergines, fresh turmeric and galangal. The fish selection is enormous; you'll find sparklingly fresh grey mullet, yellow croacker, sea bass, pomfret, squid and swordfish. The well-stocked meat counter offers prepared meats for teriyaki, such as thin slices of pork loin and belly, beef rib eye, and duck tongues and feet. Other popular products include the ready-made fish balls, fish cakes and dim sum, and store-cupboard items such as spices, sauces, rice and flour.

Cricklewood

South-East Asian Food Hall

★ WING YIP
395 Edgware Road,
London NW2 6LN
Tel: 020 8450 0422
Fax: 020 8452 1478
Website: www.wingyip.com
Open: Mon-Sat 9.30am-7pm,
Sun 11am-5.30pm **Closed:** 25, 26

Dec, Easter Sunday **Tube:** Brent Cross **Bus:** 32, 266 **Mainline station:** Cricklewood Broadway
Payment: cash, cheque, MasterCard, Visa

The sign of a good Oriental supermarket has to be whether it is popular with the local Chinese community – and this huge, one-stop supermarket certainly fits the bill. You can get everything you need for Chinese, Japanese, Thai and other Oriental cooking here, from the ingredients through to the woks and serving dishes. There is an impressive range of frozen fish and seafood, plus a wet-fish counter that often sells live crabs. You will find a dazzling array of fresh Oriental fruit, vegetables, herbs and spices (including lots of Thai ingredients), along with packaged herbs, spices, rice and noodles.

Crouch End

DUNN'S BAKERY
6 The Broadway,
London N8 9SN
Tel: 020 8340 1614
Fax: 020 8348 7856
Website:
www.dunns-bakery.co.uk
Open: Mon-Sat 7am-6pm
Closed: Sun, Bank holidays **Tube:** Finsbury Park **Bus:** W7, W5, 41
Mainline station: Hornsey
Payment: cash, cheque, Amex, Delta, Maestro, MasterCard,

British Cakes

Visa
Catalogue, Food-to-go

This enchanting shop, with its window display of children's cakes, is the place to visit for traditional, old-fashioned English baked goods and an ever-increasing range of sandwiches, savouries and salads to take away. Christopher Freeman, the fifth generation of his family to be a baker, produces a wonderful selection of organic, wholemeal and own-recipe Dunnary bread, bloomers, English cakes, tarts, biscuits and even hot-cross buns in September. The bakery is also renowned for its wedding and celebration cakes. Freeman's talents also lie in charity fund-raising – and every year he uses National Doughnut Week in April to raise money for The Children's Trust.

★ FREEMAN'S BUTCHERS

Butcher
Game dealer
Free range

9 Topsfield Parade,
London N8 8PR
Tel: 020 8340 3100
Open: Mon-Sat 8am-6pm
Closed: Sun, Bank holidays
Mainline station: Hornsey, Crouch Hill **Bus:** 41 **Payment:** cash, cheque, Maestro
Bespoke delivery

Saturday morning always sees a queue outside this popular local butcher – and deservedly so. The quality of produce and service are highly rated by serious home cooks living in this part of London. The shop sells sausages and free-range and organic meats including pork, lamb, chicken, beef and wild boar. Some of the meat products come from Black Mountain Foods in Wales, and you can also buy Martin Pitt free-range eggs. The shop is a licensed game dealer, selling pigeons and wild boar in season.

DRUMMOND STREET, NW1

In the Area Just across from Euston station, you'll find central London's Little India. Several Indian restaurants and sweet shops mingle with grocers selling Asian vegetables and fruit, packaged dried foods, herbs, spices, rice and everything else you need to make an authentic Indian or Pakistani meal. At the heart is number 119, the former site of the first retail venture by the now-famous Patak's Indian Foods.

Euston

AMBALA SWEET CENTRE

Indian
Pakistani
Confectioner

112-114 Drummond Street,
London NW1 2HN
Tel: 020 7387 3521
Open: daily 9am-9pm
Tube: Euston, Euston Square
Bus: 10, 18, 30, 68, 73, 188, 253
Payment: cash, cheque

More than 35 years ago, the first Ambala Sweet Centre was set up at this site. Today, it is an established enterprise with outlets all over the country. This shop is clean and airy, and sells a mouth-watering range of sweetmeats, including *angir, imerti, barfi* and *gulab jamun*, which is made with lentils, cashews and condensed milk. Savoury snacks include samosas and various pakora. *Jalebis* are made on the premises, while most other goods are baked in a central kitchen near Stratford.

Branches: too numerous to list here; please consult your local telephone directory.

Finchley

Japanese
Fishmonger
Grocer

★ ATARI-YA
595 High Road,
London N12 0DY
Tel: 020 8446 6669
Fax: 020 8446 6728
Open: Mon-Fri 10am-6.30pm,
Sat-Sun 10am-7pm **Tube:**
Woodside Park **Bus:** 82, 134,
260 **Payment:** cash, cheque

In spite of its rather high prices, Atari-Ya, which enjoys a sizeable Japanese clientele, is well worth a visit. There is always an excellent range of fresh fish, including bonito, turbot, yellow tail tuna and cuts especially for sushi, which are sold on Sundays. Many fish, including mackerel, pomfret and cutlass fish, come whole. For something even more exotic, try kabayaki eel, octopus scallop or black tiger prawns. The shop's freezer is stocked with squid, prawns, soba noodles and pork gyoza just like you get in Wagamama. There

are also some interesting packets on the shelves, including roasted seaweed and noodle sauces. Although everything is written in Japanese, there's always a small explanatory label in English, and the shop's staff is always happy to explain what everything is and give advice.

Branches: 7 Station Parade,
Noel Road, London W3 0DS
Tel: 020 8896 1552

15-16 Monkville Parade,
Temple Fortune, Finchley Road
London NW11 0AL
Tel: 020 8458 7626

GRAHAM'S BUTCHERS
134-136 East End Road,
London, N2 0RZ
Tel: 020 8883 6187
Open: Tues-Fri 8.30am-5pm, Sat
8am-4pm, Sun 9am-1pm **Closed:**
Mon **Tube:** East Finchley **Bus:**
82, 134, 260 **Payment:** cash,
cheque

This friendly butcher, run by the eponymous Graham and his family, was recently refitted and is now twice its original size. It is best known for its organic poultry and meat, and its fabulous range of sausages, which includes tasty varieties such as beef and horseradish. Game is on offer in season, and Graham also stocks a selection of cheeses – including organic Parmesan, organic Danish Blue and Welsh goat's cheese – plus the shop's own home-made pies.

South African
Butcher
Game dealer
Grocer
Organic

Golders Green

Jewish
Bakery
Pâtisserie
Kosher
Parev

CARMELLI BAKERIES
126-128 Golders Green Road,
London NW11 8HB
Tel: 020 8455 2074
Fax: 020 8455 2789
Open: Mon-Wed 7am-12am,
Thurs 6am-one hour before
sundown Fri, Sat one hour after
sundown-Mon 2am **Closed:** Sat,
Jewish religious holidays **Tube:**
Golders Green **Bus:** 13, 82, 260,
268 **Payment:** cash, cheque

This bustling Orthodox bakery
sells a range of bread, including
rye, granary and organic loaves,
cakes and made-up platters of
bridge rolls, sandwiches and
filled beigels. Indeed, it is the
latter that has made this bakery
famous. If none of the six listed
fillings is to your taste, the shop's
friendly staff will make up a
filling to your requirements. The
cakes come in all sizes from the
small and delicate to the large,
traditional wedding cakes and
novelty cakes for children. You'll
also find savoury items including
pizza slices, quiches and *burekas*,
plus a Parev section offering
cakes and bread that contain
eggs but no dairy products.

Hampstead

Greengrocer

BRIAN LAY-JONES
36 Heath Street,
London NW3 6TE
Tel: 020 7435 5084
Open: Mon-Sat 8am-6pm **Closed:**
Sun, Bank holidays **Tube:**
Hampstead **Bus:** 168, 268

Payment: cash, cheque
Free local delivery

This popular and well-
established greengrocer has
been in business here for
nearly two decades. It is
essentially a traditional
greengrocer, selling a range of
fruit, vegetables and herbs to
the locals, while managing to
avoid the often high prices of
the area. Not only is it a good
place to find seasonal delicacies
such as wild mushrooms or
quinces, it's also great if you
are looking for something
exotic or out of season, such as
summer berries in winter. The
staff is very friendly and offers
expert advice.

★ CARLUCCIO'S
32-34 Rosslyn Hill,
London NW3 1NH
Tel: 020 7794 2184

Main shop and branches: see
Covent Garden, page 28

Italian
Delicatessen
Café

GIACOBAZZI'S DELICATESSEN
150 Fleet Road,
London NW3 2QX
Tel: 020 7267 7222
Website:
www.giacobazzis.co.uk
Open: Mon-Fri 9.30am-7pm,
Sat 9am-6pm **Closed:** Sun, Bank
holidays. plus last two to three
weeks in August **Tube:** Belsize
Park **Bus:** 24, 46, 168, 268,
C11, C12 **Mainline station:**
Hampstead Heath **Payment:**
cash, cheque, (£5 min) Amex,

Italian
Delicatessen

Steve Hatt

Islington – *see page 146*

Super Bahar

Kensington – *see page 94*

Wembley Exotics

Wembley – *see page 135*

Arigato

Soho – *see page 51*

Maestro, MasterCard, Visa
Food-to-go

This Italian delicatessen opened its doors 10 years ago, and ever since has provided Hampstead residents with top-notch Italian produce and home-made food. As well as home-made pasta and sauces, it also sells cold meats such as San Daniele, Parma ham and bresaola; pecorino nero, buffalo mozzarella and *taleggio* cheeses; and a selection of antipasti. Prepared foods include stuffed tomatoes, baked radicchio, lasagne, *crespelli* and canelloni. The tempting desserts include Italian carrot cake, tiramisu, *panettone*, *panforte* and home-made lemon polenta cake.

Fishmonger

HAMPSTEAD SEAFOODS
78 Hampstead High Street,
London NW3 1RE
Tel: 020 7435 3966
Open: Tues-Sat 7.30am-5pm
Closed: Mon, Sun **Tube:**
Hampstead **Bus:** 168, 268
Payment: cash, cheque
Local delivery

The quality of the fish and seafood on offer at this small fishmonger is excellent. Choose from live crabs, huge jumbo prawns, shrimps or mussels, as well as sea fish such as turbot, halibut, sole (Dover and lemon), tuna, cod, swordfish – and even wild salmon and salmon trout in season. If you are in a rush, you can buy the shop's delicious, ready-cooked

lobster. The prices are very reasonable for the area.

★ MAISON BLANC
62 Hampstead High Street,
London NW3 1QH
Tel: 020 7431 8338

Main shop and branches: see
St John's Wood, page 132

PAUL
43 Hampstead High Street,
London NW3 1QG
Tel: 020 7794 8657

Main shop and branches: see
Covent Garden, page 32

ROSSLYN DELICATESSEN
56 Rosslyn Hill,
London NW3 1ND
Tel: 020 7794 9210
Fax: 020 7794 6828
Website: www.delirosslyn.co.uk
Open: Mon-Sat 8.30am-8.30pm,
Sun 8.30am-8pm **Closed:** 25, 26
Dec. **Tube:** Hampstead **Bus:** 46,
268 **Payment:** cash, cheques,
Amex, Delta, Maestro,
MasterCard, Visa

This international deli is well known for the high quality of its food. The deli counter has home-cooked meats, chickens and pizzas, plus a selection of English and European cheeses that includes lesser-known names such as Beaufort and Mimolette. There is a choice of salumi and hams, but look out for the *foie gras entier* in season if you are after a mouth-watering treat. You'll also find a

French
Bakery
Pâtisserie

French
Bakery
Pâtisserie

International
Delicatessen

> ❝ I believe that eating fresh, unprocessed, organic food provides the best nutrition available. ❞

Lynda Brown, food writer

TEN REASONS TO EAT ORGANIC

In recent years, 'organic' has become something of a culinary buzzword, most likely as a response to the food scares of the Eighties, although advocates of organic food and farming have been around for years. One notable pioneer of the organic movement is HRH The Prince of Wales, who started converting Home Farm on his estate to organic systems in 1986. However, it seems that there is still some confusion about the benefits of this way of eating. The word 'organic' brings to mind ideas of health, goodness and vitality. But what does it actually mean? And why buy organic?

- Organic food tastes good!

- Organic fruit and vegetables have been shown in a number of studies to contain more vitamins, nutrients and cancer-fighting antioxidants than non-organic food.

- Organic systems aim to avoid the use of artificial chemicals, pesticides and fertilizers.

- Organic food is produced without GMOs, which are prohibited in the Soil Association's standards for organic food and farming.

- Organic farming places great emphasis on animal welfare.

- Organic food is produced without the routine use of antibiotics.

- Organic systems reduce dependence on non-renewable resources.

- Organic production is more sustainable and friendlier to the environment and wildlife.

- There has not been a case of BSE in any herd that has been in full organic management since before 1985.

- Organic systems rely on a modern and scientific understanding of ecology and soil science, while also depending on traditional methods of crop rotations to ensure fertility and weed and pest control.

Source: The Soil Association

good range of sauces, dried pasta including spaghettini with chilli and funghi- and cuttlefish-flavoured farfalle, and high-quality olive oils from France, Italy, Spain, Greece and New Zealand. The grilled aubergine and artichoke hearts are delicious – but if you are looking for something a little different, seek out the barbecue sauces and tacos that are tucked away at the back.

Harlesden

Afro-Caribbean Food Hall

BLUE MOUNTAIN PEAK
2A-8 Craven Park Road,
London NW10 4AB
Tel: 020 8965 3859
Fax: 020 8961 0191
Open: Mon-Thurs 7.30am-6pm,
Fri and Sat 6.30am-6pm **Closed:**
Sun, Bank holidays **Tube:**
Harlesden **Bus:** 18, 206, 224,
226, 260, PR1 **Mainline station:**
Willesden Junction **Payment:**
cash, cheque, Maestro
Delivery, wholesale

Outside Brixton, this is one of the largest Afro-Caribbean food shops in London. Its fruit and vegetables – including Ugandan sweet potatoes and green bananas, chayote, mangoes, custard apples, tamarind and fresh red sorrel – are good value, as are its pulses and grains. You will find just about every hot sauce and chutney on the market, as well as plentiful supplies of Afro-Caribbean juices and concentrates, including red sorrel, mauby

syrup, bitters and herbal tea. Afro-Caribbean bread is supplemented with roti and cassava-based bammy. You'll also find patties and specially processed cheeses in the chill cabinet, plus preserved meats including dark mahogany West Indian smoked ham and garish red pickled pigs' feet, snouts and tails. The wholesale/cash-and-carry aspect of the shop ensures good value, and large-quantity provision of all manner of staples.

MORAWSKI DELICATESSEN
157 High Street,
London NW10 4RT
Tel: 020 8965 5340
Website: www.polishshops.co.uk
Open: Mon-Thurs 8am-7pm, Fri
8am-8pm, Sat 8am-6pm **Closed:**
Sun, Bank holidays **Tube:**
Willesden Junction **Bus:** 18, 224,
266 **Mainline station:** Willesden
Junction **Payment:** cash, cheque,
Amex, Delta, Maestro,
MasterCard, Visa

Polish Central European Grocer

This is a Polish/Continental shop of the old order. It is well stocked with food beloved of the central European community but also attracts those who have developed a taste for the rather good charcuterie and range of fruit syrups, preserves and sweetmeats. You'll find innumerable brands of pickled gherkins and *sauerkraut*, each subtly different and with its own adherents. More rarified are the tinned carp and jars of apple paprika, *aivar* (a red pepper sauce) and bean salads, which are stocked alongside containers of herring fillets in sour cream and other sauces. There are also plenty of black and other rye loaves and sweetmeats here, including spiced biscuits and delicious chocolate-coated plums. The sausages – specifically *krakowska, sopocka, krajana* and *wiejska* – are superb, as are the fruit and vegetable juices, which come in distinctly un-British combinations such as beetroot and apple. The shop also carries Polish beers and wines, and offers freshly made coffee, sandwichs and pastries,

Highgate

Delicatessen

KALENDAR
15A Swain's Lane,
London N6 6QX
Tel/Fax: 020 8348 8300
Open: Mon-Fri 8am-10am, Sat and Sun 9am-10pm
Tube: Tufnell Park
Bus: 214
Mainline Station: Gospel Oak, Hampstead Heath
Payment: cash, cheque, Amex, Delta, Maestro, MasterCard, Visa
Food-to-go

After running the neighbouring Café Mozart for seven years, owner Alex Dudnic launched this popular deli-café with the goal of sharing his favourite foods. The deli counter is packed with meats from nearby butcher Elite Meats, Neal's Yard Dairy cheeses (page 31), Flour Power City bread and moreish desserts. Some of these, such as the fruit crumbles and sticky toffee pudding, are made on site, while others are supplied by Konditor & Cook (page 156). You can get brewed coffee from Monmouth Coffee Company, too (page 30), and freshly made juices and smoothies. All of this, combined with the café's delicious all-day breakfasts, has made Kalendar a firm favourite with locals. (Celebrity chef and Camden resident Giorgio Locatelli regularly drops by.) They'll no doubt be delighted to hear that Dudnic plans to devote the present site to the café and open a full-scale deli down the road.

Kentish Town

B & M SEAFOODS/THE PURE MEAT COMPANY
258 Kentish Town Road,
London NW5 2AA
Tel/Fax: 020 7485 0346
Open: Mon-Sat 8am-5.30pm
Closed: Sun, Bank holidays **Tube:** Kentish Town **Bus:** C2, 134, 135, 214 **Payment:** cash, cheque, Amex, Delta, Maestro, MasterCard, Solo, Visa
Free local delivery

Organic
Butcher
Fishmonger
Game Dealer
Delicatessen

It is not often that you come across a business that does so many things so well. As well as being an organic butcher and a fishmonger that sells only fresh, wild and organic fish, this shop also sells high-quality poultry, game and delicatessen items. The fish are stacked up in a colourful design at the back of the shop, with chillers to the side containing organic beef, pork, lamb, duck, chicken, pheasants and home-made sausages. A speciality is smoked fish. The deli features a good range of cooked meats, pies and cheeses, including a highly recommended Cornish cheese.

Wholefood
Organic
Grocer

BUMBLEBEE NATURAL FOODS
30, 32, 33 Brecknock Road,
London N7 0DD
Tel/Fax: 020 7607 1936
Website: www.bumblebee.co.uk
Open: Mon-Wed, Fri-Sat 9am-6.30pm, Thurs 9am-7.30pm
Closed: Sun, Bank holidays **Tube:** Kentish Town, Tufnell Park **Bus:** 29, 253, 390 **Payment:** cash, cheque, Amex, Delta, Maestro, MasterCard, Visa
Bespoke delivery, food-to-go, online ordering, vegetable box scheme

In business for more than 20 years, Bumblebee is one of London's largest independent retailers of vegetarian, organic and wholefood products. It is spread across three premises: number 30 stocks a vast selection of dried products,

while number 32 offer home-baked goodies such as brownies, croissants and gluten-free bread, and an extensive selection of organic beers and wines. You'll also find a good deli section with foods to take away, and a range of sweets, chocolates and Helsett Farm organic ice creams here. Number 33 is just across the road and stocks a wholly organic range of fresh fruit, vegetables, herbs and spices.

FISH AND FOWL
145 Highgate Road,
London NW5 1LJ
Tel: 020 7284 4184
Fax: 020 7482 1500
Open: Fri and Sat 9.30am-5pm
Closed: Sun, Mon-Thurs (but knock on the shutters before midday and you may get served), Bank holidays **Tube:** Kentish Town, Tufnell Park
Bus: C2, 214, C11 **Payment:** cash, cheque, Delta, Maestro, MasterCard, Visa
Catering

Fishmonger
Poulterer

Customers visiting this shop can be assured of absolute freshness – the shop has a wholesale side that services some of London's top restaurants, including The Eagle, Nicole's at Nicole Farhi, Camden Brasserie and Orso, among others. As proprietor Adrian Rudolf used to work in a restaurant kitchen, customers can also get advice on how to cook anything they buy.

Italian
Delicatessen

SALVINO

47 Brecknock Road,
London N7 0BT
Tel: 020 7267 5305
Open: Mon-Sat 8.30am-7pm
Closed: Sun, Bank holidays
Tube: Kentish Town, Tufnell
Park **Bus:** 29, 253, 390 **Payment:**
cash, cheque, Amex, Delta,
Maestro, MasterCard, Solo, Visa
Catering, local delivery

This good Italian deli has been
in business for more than two
decades and is run by brothers
Antonio and Stefano Salvino,
who hail from Sicily. It operates
as both a basic, neighbourhood
food store stocking high-quality
Italian groceries as well as a
place for fresh, imported
cheeses, salume and olives. You
will find Sicilian pecorino, baby
cipolle (onions in Balsamic
vinegar) and mascarpone
layered with pine nuts, basil and
Parmesan. Parma ham is sliced
for you to order, along with
fennel salami and other meats.
The Salvinos also stock a small
organic range, which includes
free-range eggs, some wines,
fresh herbs and pizzas. Be sure
to pick up some handmade
lobster tortellini, then browse
the shelves for excellent olive oil
from Seggiano, an Italian
liqueur, some cantucci biscuits,
pasta or perhaps just a jar of
Italian *passata*. The shop holds
occasional Saturday tastings and
special events.

Kilburn

★ THE OLIVE TREE

84 Willesden Lane,
London NW6 7TA
Tel: 020 7328 9078
Open: Mon, Tues, Thurs-Sat
10am-6.30pm, Wed 1pm-7pm.
Closed: Sun **Tube:** Kilburn,
Kilburn Park **Bus:** 98 **Mainline
station:** Brondesbury, Kilburn
High Road **Payment:** cash,
cheque, Delta, Mestro,
MasterCard, Visa

This tiny shop is packed from
floor to ceiling with every kind
of organic food except fish and
meat. Your eye will immediately
be caught by a selection of
pristine fruit and vegetables,
most of which are seasonal
British, although there are
sometimes unusual items such
as mini avocados or custard
apples. The owner, Costas
Papantoniou, gets much of his
produce from New Covent
Garden. 'It's the only way to
guarantee the best,' he says. On
Fridays, he also receives a
delivery of fresh organic fruit
and veg from Chris Baur of
Ripple Farm, near Canterbury
(he also supplies Bumblebee,
page 125, and Planet Organic,
page 16). Papantoniou makes a
particular effort to stock good
bread, some of which comes
from The Celtic Baker and
Neal's Yard Bakery. Groceries
include gluten-free puffed spelt,
flour, fresh yeast, nuts, honeys,
olive oils and olives.

Wholefood
Greengrocer
Grocer
Organic

Food Hall
Grocer
Delicatessen

Maida Vale

THE ORGANIC GROCER
17 Clifton Road,
London W9 1SY
Tel: 020 7286 1400
Fax: 020 7286 2717
Open: Mon-Sat 9am-8pm, Sun
10am-8pm **Closed:** Bank
holidays **Tube:** Warwick Avenue
Bus: 6 **Payment:** cash, cheque,
Delta, Maestro, MasterCard,
Visa, Amex
Food-to-go

This small shop enjoys a loyal
following in the pleasant
shopping district of Maida Vale.
Over 95% of the mini
supermarket's stock is organic,
and it sells fresh fish delivered
daily from the Isle of Man, dairy
products, pasta, sweets, cereals
and a variety of health foods. A
juice bar serves fresh fruit and
vegetable juices, and a resident
chef prepares two fresh pasta
sauces and takeaway food daily.
The shop also stocks a good
range of organic wines and beers.

Muswell Hill

Cheese shop

CHEESES
13 Fortis Green Road,
London N10 3HP
Tel: 020 8444 9141
Open: Tues-Sat 9.45am-5.45pm,
Closed: Mon, Sun **Tube:**
Highgate **Bus:** 43, 102, 134, 234
Mainline station: Wood Green,
Alexandra Palace **Payment:**
cash, cheque, Delta, Maestro,
MasterCard, Visa
Local delivery

This tiny, wedge-shaped shop
may be difficult to find from the
Muswell Hill Broadway end of
the street, but it is well worth
seeking out. Established more
than 20 years ago, and run by
its present owner, Vanessa
Wiley, for 12 of them, it is a
firm favourite with local
residents. They come for
Wiley's expertise and the
superb range of cheeses, which
are always at exactly the right
stage of maturity. You will find
classics such as 18-month-old
Montgomery Cheddar, salmon
pink Appleby Cheshire and
Gorwydd Caerphilly (one of
Wiley's favourites), plus more
unusual varieties including
Tomme de Véran, a goat's
cheese from Lyon that is only
available during the summer
months, and 18-month-old
Beaufort, a delicious farmhouse
Gruyère made with spring milk.
Wiley also carries a fantastic
range of accessories including
beautiful slate cheese boards
and whitewashed, wood
cheese larders, as well as tasty
biscuits, relishes and James
chocolates. Queues are long
on Saturdays so a weekday visit
is recommended.

W. MARTYN
135 Muswell Hill Broadway,
London N10 3RS
Tel: 020 8883 5642
Open: Mon-Wed 9.30am-
5.30pm, Thurs 9.30am-1pm, Fri
9.30am-5.30pm, Sat 9am-
5.30pm **Closed:** Sun, Bank
holidays **Bus:** 43, 134 **Payment:**

Coffee
Tea

cash, cheque, Maestro, Mastercard, Visa

The aroma of freshly roasted coffee that greets you as you walk through the door of this popular tea and coffee shop is truly intoxicating. Founded by the present owner's great-great grandfather in 1897, the shop still has a real turn-of-the-century feel, with wooden shelves and old balance scales on the counter and photographs of the original shop on the walls. As well as its range of freshly ground coffee, the shop also sells a selection of fine foods including jams, marmalades, tea, pickles, relishes, pâtés, marinades and vinegar; old-fashioned sweets; and fresh cakes from Dunn's (page 117).

Fishmonger
Poulterer

WALTER PURKIS & SONS
52 Muswell Hill Broadway,
London N10 3RT
Tel: 020 8883 4355
Open: Tues-Sat 8.30pm-5pm
Closed: Sun, Mon **Tube:**
Highgate **Bus:** 43, 102, 134, 234
Mainline station: Wood Green,
Alexandra Palace **Payment:** cash,
cheque, Amex, Delta, Maestro,
MasterCard, Visa

Walter Purkis has remained popular with Muswell Hill shoppers for more than a generation. Indeed, the opening of a Marks & Spencer foodstore just along the road has made no difference at all to its trade. 'The supermarkets buy in bulk, and the best fish doesn't come in bulk. My customers know that,' says Purkis. Each morning, he travels to Billingsgate and buys a wide selection of fish, including cockles, mussels, crabs, scallops, oysters, sprats, mackerel, monkfish, red and grey mullet, halibut, sea bass and wild salmon in season. Purkis's second shop down the hill has a smoke-house where, for both shops, he produces smoked trout, haddock, tuna, his own dyed and undyed kippers, and smokies, which he first tried at the suggestion of a customer a few years ago and has continued to sell ever since. On occasion, Purkis also hot-smokes halibut and mussels. The shop's other temptations include a growing range of deli-fresh, fish-related products and marinades.

Branch: 17 The Broadway,
London N8 8DU
Tel: 020 8340 6281

Primrose Hill

★ **MELROSE & MORGAN**
42 Gloucester Avenue,
London NW1 8JD
Tel: 020 7722 0011
Website:
www.melroseandmorgan.com
Open: Tues–Sat 9am–8pm, Sun
10am–6pm **Closed:** Mon
Tube: Chalk Farm, Camden
Town **Bus:** 274 **Mainline station:**
Kentish Town West
Payment: cash, cheque, Amex,
Delta, Maestro, MasterCard,
Visa

British
Grocer

Le Marrakech

Notting Hill – *see page 102*

Panzer's

St John's Wood – *see page 133*

La Fromagerie

Highbury – *see page 141*

Planet Organic

Bayswater – *see page 16*

Catering, food-to-go, cakes to order

Ian James and Nick Selby opened Melrose & Morgan in 2004 with the modest aim of providing a proper corner shop. 'We looked around and thought, "Why can't there be a shop that serves the best seasonal, traceable produce and is open six days a week?"' says James. But Melrose and Morgan is a far cry from the average convenience store. An arresting glass-fronted façade gives way to an airy interior, where an open kitchen churns out tantalising soups, savoury pies, stewed fruit and ready meals. You'll also find a carefully chosen selection of mainly British foods. 'We wanted to reduce choice for our customers,' explains James. The vast central table, then, displays four peak-perfection cheeses from Neal's Yard (page 31), two types of honey from The Hive Honey Shop (page 174) and a smattering of iced cupcakes from the nearby Primrose Bakery. Flour Station and Breads Etcetera supply the loaves and the currant and Chelsea buns, while the fresh fruit and vegetables come from organic wholesalers and New Covent Garden Market. Devoted customers – and there are many, clustering around the kitchen counter for a chat and advice on food preparation – will soon benefit from a home-delivery scheme. But until then, they can master the Melrose & Morgan ethos at its recently launched cookery classes.

Queens Park

★ BAKER & SPICE
75 Salusbury Road,
London NW6 6NH
Tel: 020 7604 3636

Main shop and branch: see
Chelsea, page 20

Bakery
Delicatessen
Pâtisserie

St John's Wood

BREAD SHOP
65 St John's Wood High Street,
London NW8 7NL
Tel/Fax: 020 7586 5311
Website: www.breadshop.co.uk
Open: Mon-Fri 7am-6.30pm, Sat 7am-6pm, Sun 8am-5pm **Tube:** St John's Wood **Bus:** 13, 46, 82, 113 **Payment:** cash, cheque
Bespoke deliveries locally, online ordering service

Continental
Bakery

Appalled by the lack of good bread in England 10 years ago, Jonathan Cohen launched the Bread Shop with the simple aim of turning buying bread into a 'pleasure rather than a daily chore'. The shop's fresh, modern design is a delight: the self-service hopper pillars are decorated with swirls of colourful grains and pulses, and the shopping baskets are paper-lined willow. You'll find 40 different types of organic bread, most of which is crunchy-crusted and multi-grained. While Germanic flours and styles (*Saatenbrot, Kartoffelkruste, 7 Körner brot*) predominate, there are also airy ciabattas, flaky teacakes, the lightest and crunchiest of pretzels and a wheat-free spelt product range that includes delicious croissants. If you can't make it to one of the Bread Shop's two branches, you'll also find its bread at Selfridges (page 43), Harrods (page 33) and Planet Organic (page 16).

Branch: see Chiswick, page 76

Fishmonger

BROWN'S

37-39 Charlbert Street,
London NW8 6JN
Tel: 020 7722 8237/6284
Fax: 020 7483 0502
Open: Tues-Sat 8am-5.30pm
Closed: Sun, Mon, Bank
holidays **Tube:** St John's Wood
Bus: 13, 46, 82, 113 **Payment:**
cash, cheque, Amex, Delta,
Mastro, MasterCard, Visa
Bespoke home deliveries locally

This excellent, family-run fish merchant has been in business for more than 50 years and is widely recognized as having some of the best fish and seafood in London. Hand-picked supplies of Cornish sea bass, wild Irish salmon, Dover and lemon soles, Scotch halibut and turbot are always available. You'll also find Scotch lobsters, Cornish crabs and fresh, raw shrimp and scallops, plus Scotch smoked salmon, naturally smoked haddock and manx, and loch kippers. All are prepared on the premises to customer specifications, and the friendly, helpful staff is always happy to provide recipes and cooking advice.

Italian
Delicatessen
Café

★ CARLUCCIO'S

60 St John's Wood High Street,
London NW8 7SH
Tel: 020 7449 0404

Main shop and branches: see Covent Garden, page 28

COASTLINE

69 Abbey Road,
London NW8 0AE
Tel/Fax: 020 7624 9984
Open: Tues-Fri 9am-5pm, Sat
9am-3pm **Closed:** Sun, Mon, day
following Bank holidays **Tube:** St
John's Wood **Bus:** 139, 189
Mainline station: Kilburn High
Road **Payment:** cash, cheque,
Amex, Delta, Maestro,
MasterCard, Visa
Bespoke deliveries

Fishmonger

Although a little out on a limb, this small fish shop is well worth a visit. As well as fresh seafood,

As long as a day without bread.

French expression for a tedious passage of time

you will get friendly and knowledgeable service from seven times British oyster-opening champion Armando Lema, who sources his oysters from Rossmore in Cork. Meticulous attention is paid to dressing crabs and lobsters, and preparing seafood platters (order ahead for a party) – with delivery to almost anywhere in London via the wholesale arm of the company, Coastline Galicia. In addition to the fresh fish, you will also find a small stock of frozen seafood including langoustines and prawns, smoked fish such as sprats and Loch Fyne salmon, salt cod, marinated anchovies and a good range of bottled soups – plus a selection of sauces and pickles.

Delicatessen
Persian/
Turkish
Greengrocer
Organic

IMAN FOOD STORE

77 Abbey Road,
London NW8 0AE
Tel: 020 7372 1100
Fax: 020 7328 2139
Open: Mon-Sun 8am-9pm
Closed: Bank holidays **Tube:**
St John's Wood **Bus:** 139, 189
Payment: cash, cheque, Amex,
Maestro, MasterCard, Visa
Food-to-go

A few doors along from Coastline is this smart venture owned and run by Persian-born Zari Mohseni and family. Natural surfaces make a good background to display the beautifully packaged, carefully sourced fresh and home-cooked food on sale here. Mohseni is

proud of her handmade baklava and Persian sweets, some of which are unique to London. High-quality French cheeses, organic dairy produce, bread from Poilâne (page 19) and & Clarke's (page 92) – there are plans to introduce a traditional oven where flatbread (*lavash*) will be made – fresh fruit and vegetables, organic, handmade dried pasta and interesting preserves, oils and vinegars jostle for space with *torshi* (pickles), dips, dried limes and other fruit, nuts, saffron and fresh dates. The fridge is stocked with goodies made daily on the premises, including houmous, taramasalata and salads, as well as *traiteur* food including roast fresh salmon and Persian classics *faisenjan* (chicken cooked with walnuts and pomegranates), *ghormeh sabzi* (chicken and beans flavoured with herbs and dried limes) and *havich polo* (a carrot-based chicken rice salad flavoured with *zereshk*). Downstairs, there is a mini-market for daily essentials. A branch in Kensington Church Street is in the pipeline.

KENT & SONS

Butcher

59 St John's Wood High Street,
London NW8 7NL
Tel: 020 7722 2258
Website: www.kents-butchers.co.uk
Open: Mon-Sat 8am-5.45pm
Closed: Sun, Bank holidays
Tube: St John's Wood **Bus:** 13,
46, 82, 113 **Payment:** cash,
cheque, Delta, Maestro,

MasterCard, Solo, Visa

Accounts accepted, bespoke deliveries locally

Although this Q-guild butcher has been in business for some 80 years, the premises still have a sparkling, modern feel. The shop's meat is of superlative quality: free-range and organic chickens and lamb (cuts include racks of lamb and French trimmed cutlets) are sourced from the West country and Welsh Black Mountain Foods; free-range pork comes from East Anglia; and the organic beef and mince are grass-fed Aberdeen Angus. There is also game to be had in season, plus Dutch calf's liver, English lamb's liver, boiling fowl, home-cooked hams and chickens, and English and Continental cheeses. The glass chill cabinet reveals a wide range of daily-changing, kitchen-ready preparations, such as breaded veal escalopes, chicken and lamb kebabs, lemon and coriander satays, chicken fillets in yoghurt marinade and excellent burgers. The service is unfailingly helpful and friendly.

French
Bakery
Pâtisserie

★ MAISON BLANC

37 St John's Wood High Street,
London NW8 7NJ
Tel: 020 7586 1982
Fax: 020 7586 1087
Website:
www.maisonblanc.com
Open: Mon-Sat 8am-7pm, Sun
9am-6.30pm **Tube:** St John's

Wood **Bus:** 13, 46, 82, 113
Payment: cash, cheque, Delta,
Maestro, MasterCard,
Visa

This popular boulangerie/ pâtisserie, which has branches dotted around the capital, is as popular with local French residents as it is with those seeking to recreate their holiday memories. Everything is made on a daily basis, using French flour and traditional methods – and most of the qualified chefs and shop staff are French. The bread is baked in stone ovens and is free from fat and additives; *baguettes de tradition* are the most popular loaves, but other varieties, including *pain de campagne, pain au levain* and *pain aux olives,* are well worth tasting. Maison Blanc also stocks the traditional viennoiserie that one associates with France – *croissants, pain au chocolat* and *brioche*, to name a few – as well as a variety of mouth-watering pâtisserie and savouries to eat in the tea-room or take away. Of the many fruit tarts, the bestsellers are *tarte au citron* and the delicious *fraisier*.

At Christmas, try the traditional *Bûche de Noël*, followed by the *Galette des Rois* for the Epiphany. Maison Blanc also makes a range of five wedding cakes to order and sells a selection of chocolates, truffles and other sweet things.

Branches: see Chelsea, page 25, Chiswick, page 78, Fulham, page 84, Hampstead page 121, Holland Park page 90, Kensington, page 93, Putney, page 183, Richmond page 184

Jewish Delicatessen Kosher Parev

★ PANZER'S

13-19 Circus Road,
London NW8 6PB
Tel: 020 7722 8596/8162
Fax: 020 7586 0209
Website: www.panzers.co.uk
Open: Mon-Fri 8am-7pm, Sat 8am-6pm, Sun 8am-2pm **Closed:** Bank holidays **Tube:** St John's Wood **Bus:** 13, 46, 82, 113
Payment: cash, cheque, Delta, Maestro, MasterCard, Visa
Delivery, food-to-go, mail order

It is at Panzer's excellent charcuterie and fish counters that the Jewish flavour of the shop's neighbourhood is most apparent. At the fish counter, whole sides of smoked salmon are there for the slicing, and you can choose to have it on the oily or dry side. There are also *latkes*, *gefilte* fish, kippers, sprats, huge bowls of marinated olives, and cooked and preserved meats galore. While it stocks a wide range of conventional vegetables, fruit, herbs and spices – 12 salad leaf

varieties, 10 kinds of tomatoes, 10 types of berries and 22 kinds of fresh herbs – Panzer's also prides itself on being able to source any goods from around the world, even out of season. Look out for persimmons, galangal, velvet-black figs, purple basil and plump pods of tamarind. Inside, alongside conventional groceries, are many lines that cater to the varied communities that have gravitated to St John's Wood. There are American products that you'll find nowhere else, and one corner of the store specializes in Japanese foods such as rice, dried seaweed and shiitake, miso and giant bottles of Kikkoman soy sauce. Another corner is dedicated to the fast-selling, in-store-baked bread, which includes delicious beigels.

RIAS ALTAS

97 Frampton Street,
London NW8 8NA
Tel: 020 7262 4340
Open: Mon-Sat 9.30am-7.30pm
Closed: Sun, Bank holidays **Tube:** Warwick Avenue **Bus:** 6, 16, 98
Payment: cash, cheque, Delta, Maestro, MasterCard, Visa

Spanish Delicatessen

This wonderful shop stocks all things Spanish – from *jamón serrano* and manchego to paella pans, earthenware *cazuelas* and even cosmetics. Canned foods abound: you'll find white asparagus, Albo seafoods and classics including *fabada asturiana* and *callos con garbanzos* – plus huge tins of olives, oils and rice for paella. The fresh food counter carries hams, chorizos and fresh cheeses. The Spanish sweet tooth is well catered for, too, with shelf upon shelf of biscuits and cakes such as *mantecadas* and *tortas de aceite*, and sweetmeats including *roscos de vino* and *turron*. Be sure to try the bespoke sandwiches filled with cheese or *jamón*, and the delicious home-made Spanish tortilla (available at lunchtime only). Sound bread, Portuguese pastries and a good range of wines, brandies and liqueurs complete the picture.

Swiss Cottage

Chocolate

ACKERMANS
9 Goldhurst Terrace,
London NW6 3HX
Tel/Fax: 020 7624 2742
Open: Mon-Fri 10am-6pm, Sat 9.30am-5pm **Closed:** Sun (open Bank Holidays) **Tube:** Swiss Cottage, Finchley Road **Bus:** 13, 31, 82, 113, C11 **Mainline station:** South Hampstead, Frognal **Payment:** cash, cheque, Amex, Delta, Maestro, MasterCard, Solo, Visa
International mail order

Ackermans, which holds a Royal Appointment, is regarded by many as England's finest chocolatier – if only on account of its superb dark chocolate 'thins'. The shop preserves a family-run feel – even if you simply want to buy a tiny sample in a plain cellophane bag, the

service is charming and helpful. The mere aroma, however, is likely to inspire a larger purchase. Ackermans stocks Norhouse, Godiva and other brands that don't make the mail order list. Be sure to try the 100s and 1000s, for example, or the fragile brandy-soaked cherries enrobed, stem and all, in dark chocolate.

Branch: see Docklands, page 160

Wembley

★ LOON FUNG
1 Glacier Way,
London HA0 1HQ
Tel: 020 8810 8188

Chinese Food Hall

Main shop and branch: see Chinatown, page 27

★ V.B. & SONS
147 Ealing Road,
London HAO 4BU
Tel: 020 8785 0387
Fax: 020 8902 8579
Open: Mon-Fri 9.30am-6.45pm, Sat 9am-6.45pm, Sun 11am-5pm **Closed:** Christmas **Tube:** Alperton **Bus:** 79, 83, 224, 297 **Mainline station:** Wembley Central **Payment:** cash, cheque, Amex, Delta, Mestro, MasterCard, Visa

Indian Grocer

If you are planning to cook an Indian feast for a large number, this is the place to visit to stock up on dried herbs, spices, rice, pulses and general Indian ingredients. This is also where many Asian shop owners and restaurateurs shop, so most ingredients are sold in large quantities. Consequently, there are good bargains to be had, and you'll find unusual snacks such as bite-sized poppadums and cassava chips, plus packaged mixes to make Indian bread or sweets including *gulab jamun*. Look in the frozen-food cabinet for frozen *parathas* and ready-made meals, as well as some of the more exotic vegetables.

Indian
Greengrocer

★ WEMBLEY EXOTICS LTD
133-135 Ealing Road,
London HA0 4BP
Tel: 020 8900 2607
Fax: 020 8900 1669
Open: daily 24 hours **Tube:** Alperton **Bus:** 79, 83, 224, 297 **Mainline station:** Wembley Central **Payment:** cash, cheque, Amex, Delta, Maestro, MasterCard, Visa

Don't let the somewhat ordinary selection of everyday fresh fruit and stacks of garlic outside fool you – inside, this 24-hour greengrocer turns into a cornucopia of the most wonderful and exotic fruit from all over the world. Depending on the season, you'll be able to find small apple bananas, yellow and black passion fruit, jackfruit, mangosteens, rambutans and guava, as well as mangoes in just about every size and colour. This is also the place to visit for out-of-the ordinary vegetables including Thai yard-long beans, cassava, sweet potatoes, East African kontola drumsticks and all types of aubergines. The shop also stocks karela, dudhi, tindori and an annual supply of fresh chickpeas, which Madhur Jaffrey describes as a 'treat not to be missed'. Locally made Indian pickles such as carrot and lime are popular, as is the range of even hotter pickles.

LEGEND

- ▬▬ Motorway
- ▬▬ Main Road
- ▬▬ Other Road
- Highbury & Islington ● Railway Station
- ⊖ Underground
- Waterways
- 🌳 Parks

| 0 | | | | | 1000m |
| 0 | | | | | 1000yd |

South Woodford

SOUTH WOODFORD

High Rd

High Rd

A406

BROADMEAD RD

M11

South Woodford

George La

WOODFORD AVE

HERMON HILL

A406

WOODFORD RD

WOODFORD NEW RD

Wood St Walthamstow

Snaresbrook Rd

SNARESBROOK

HOLLYBUSH HILL

NEW WANSTEAD

Snaresbrook

High Street

WHIPPS CROSS RD

James Lane

CAMBRIDGE PARK

EASTERN AVE

Wanstead

NORTH CIRCULAR

WOODFORD AVE

WANSTEAD

Rd

Leytonstone

BUSH RD

BLAKE HALL RD

Wanstead Park

LEYTONSTONE

ALDERSBROOK RD

HIGH RD LEYTONSTONE

Harrow Rd

CENTRE RD

Wanstead Flats

Cann Hall Rd

Dames Rd

WOODFORD RD

Forest Lane

COBHAM RD

Wanstead Park

ROMFORD RD

Leyton Rd

Water La

ROMFORD RD

Green St

Stratford

Katherine Rd

WEST HAM LANE

UPTON LANE

Vicarage La

Portway

Plashet Rd

Upton Park

Green St

PLASHET RD

Plaistow

BARKING RD

West Ham

MANOR RD

PLAISTOW

Balaam St

BARKING RD

Stephenson St

PRINCE REGENT

NEWHAM WAY

Dalston

Turkish
Food Hall
Halal

TURKISH FOOD CENTRE
89 Ridley Road,
London E8 2NP
Tel: 020 7254 6754
Open: Mon-Sat 8am-9pm, Sun
8.30am-7.30pm **Mainline station:**
Dalston Kingsland **Bus:** 30, 56,
Payment: cash, Maestro, Visa

This popular food hall is set out like a supermarket and offers an extensive range of Turkish products. The quality of the fruit and vegetables is high – but the selection changes frequently, as the shop only sells what is seasonally available. You'll find great bunches of fresh herbs as well as long green chillies, tomatoes, peppers, aubergines, white courgettes, quinces and prickly pears. Sacks of pistachios, rice and dried pulses line the walls. The cheese counter offers excellent natural Greek yoghurts, fetas and halloumi, as well as prepacked cheeses and several types of marinated olives. The bakery produces fresh flatbread and sesame bread, plus a good selection of sweet pastries including baklava. At the halal meat counter, look out for fresh lamb, goat and chicken.

Branches: see Catford, page 160, Lewisham, page 167, Leytonstone, page 147, Tottenham, page 150

Ridley Road Market

Open: Mon-Sat 7am-5pm,
Mainline station: Dalston Kingsland
Bus: 30, 38, 56, 67, 76, 106, 149

Otherwise known as Dalston Market, this traditional East End street market is best on Fridays and Saturdays. The narrow market, which lines a street of lock-up shops, throbs to the varying ethnic rhythms emanating from music stalls, and the foods on offer are similarly varied. (The beigel shop alone offers jerk chicken, chilli tuna and salt beef beigels.) Among everyday fruit and vegetables, which are sometimes offered in a bargain scoop – three mangoes for £1 – are colourful pyramids of Afro-Caribbean specialities, including jackfruit, soursops, yams, plantains, ready-made hot sauces, dried and smoked fish, and cooked snacks. Turkish herbs and other foodstuffs are on offer as well. Many of the stalls reflect the cosmopolitan nature of the area and the market, selling unfamiliar parts of familiar animals, halal meat, seafood from warm waters (king fish, tilapia, flying fish, snappers and croakers), as well as clothes, beauty products, kitchenware and other household goods.

Hackney

Delicatessen

L'EAU À LA BOUCHE
49 Broadway Market,
London E8 4PH
Tel: 020 7923 0600
Website: www.labouche.co.uk
Open: Mon-Fri 9am-7pm, Sat
9am-5pm, Sun 10am-4pm
Tube: Bethnal Green
Bus: D6, 26, 48, 55, 106, 254,
277, 388, 394
Mainline station: Cambridge
Heath, London Fields
Payment: cash, cheque, Delta,
Electron, Maestro, MasterCard,
Visa
Food-to-go

Frenchman Stef Cusset opened
this deli-café following the
closure of Stoke Newington's
The Cooler, where he was
manager. That store's still-
stricken customers regularly
make the trek to L'Eau à la
Bouche to stock up their
fridges, alongside local residents
and the artists whose studios
dot the area. They can buy
practically everything here.
Belying its small size, the shop
stocks pantry staples, often with
a French twist; charcuterie from
a range of small suppliers;
French cheeses, which are
delivered each week; bread
from Born & Bread (page 161);
and a selection of mid-priced
wines. Somehow, there's still
room for a table piled high with
fat olives and Belle Epoque and
Nomad cakes and pastries, and
a child-friendly café. Here,
customers can order sandwiches
made from any anything that's
carried in the shop. Saturday,
when the shop has a
Broadway Market stall
stocking three times its usual
supply of cheeses, is a great
day to visit.

Harringay

Turkish
Pâtisserie
Confectioner

ANTEPLILER
47 Grand Parade, Green
Lanes, London N4 1AG
Tel: 020 8809 1004
Fax: 020 8809 1003
Open: daily 10am-10pm **Tube:**
Turnpike Lane, Manor House
Bus: 29, 141, 341 **Mainline
station:** Harringay West
Payment: cash, cheque

This Turkish confectioner has
a wonderful selection of
pastries, all of which are made
on the premises by a staff of
seven, including the owner,
Ahmet Ustunsumeli.
Everything is coated with
syrup, which means that it is
incisively sweet – but thanks
to Ustunsumeli and his team's
light touch, it is also delicate
and surprisingly refreshing.
Especially recommended are
sobiyet, little crescents of very
thin filo pastry filled with
shredded pistachios and
cream; *burma*, a filo pastry roll
generously stuffed with
chopped pistachios; and
kadayif, a spectacular, crisp
burnished tart about a yard
across made of pistachios and
konafa. Prices are by weight
and are very reasonable.

Greek
Bakery
Pâtisserie
Celebration
Cakes

Turkish
Bakery
Pâtisserie
Grocer
Greengrocer

Branch: see Newington Green, page 147

BARNABY'S

8A Grand Parade, Green Lanes, London N4 1JX
Tel: 020 8802 0275
Open: Mon-Sat 8am-10pm, Sun 10am-8pm **Tube:** Turnpike Lane, Manor House **Bus:** 29, 141, 341 **Mainline station:** Harringay West
Payment: cash, cheque

Barnaby's is a Greek bakery, but it owes its enormous popularity as much to its birthday cakes as its baklava and bread. The front part of the shop is given over to various Greek pastries such as *shiamali, shiamishi*, and *lokoumades*, and savoury items including buns stuffed with halloumi, *koubes* (minced lamb rolls) and sesame, tahini, and olive bread. (You will often see assistants chopping olives by the kitchen door.) At the back, British tastes are catered for with fruit tarts, cream slices, chocolate éclairs and impressive celebration cakes: frozen ones can be bought directly, or fresh ones – of any kind and decorated according to fancy – can be ordered.

Branch: 34 Green Lanes, London N13 6 HT
Tel: 020 8889 4324

★ YASAR HALIM

493-495 Green Lanes, London N4 1AL
Tel: 020 8340 8090
Open: Mon-Sun 8am-10pm

Closed: Bank holidays **Tube:** Manor House, Turnpike Lane **Bus:** 29, 141 **Mainline station:** Harringay Green Lanes
Payment: cash, cheque, Maestro,

This popular bakery is well known for its traditional wedding and birthday cakes. You'll also find a tempting selection of cakes, bread and large and small pastries, such as *lokma* (honey balls). Be sure to try the spinach and cheese pies made with pastry rather than filo, and the home-made rice pudding. The grocery section sells everything you need for Turkish cooking, with seasonal specialities including black-eyed beans, *colocassi* and colourful sweet peppers.

Branch: see Shepherd's Bush, page 110

Highbury

CECIL & CO.

393 Liverpool Road, London N1 1NP
Tel: 020 7700 6707
Fax: 020 7700 5738
Open: Tues-Fri 8am-3.30pm
Closed: Sun, Bank holidays **Tube:** Highbury & Islington
Bus: 40 **Payment:** cash, cheque, Delta, Maestro, MasterCard, Visa

The Doyle family has moved its retail

Fishmonger

shop from Mayfair up to Highbury, where it now shares its premises with the wholesale side of the business. The shop stocks an excellent range of fresh fish, as you would expect from a fishmonger that holds two Royal Appointments. The smoked fish on offer includes haddock, halibut, trout and eel fillets, kippers, oysters, mussels and salmon. You'll also find a fine range of ready-prepared, fishy products, such as lobster butter, fish soups and *fonds*, colourful fish terrines designed for dinner parties and, of course, caviar. Related culinary delights include artisanal confits, dried mushrooms, innovative salad dressings and, not least, Ellie-Arnaud Denoix Cognacs, Eaux de Vie and grappas in elegant bottles. The staff is charming and, even when the shop is closed on Mondays and Saturdays, is happy for you to wander round to the wholesale entrance to be served there.

Butcher
Game dealer
Free range
Organic

★ FRANK GODFREY

7 Highbury Park,
London N5 1QJ
Tel: 020 7226 2425
Fax: 020 7263 8016
Website: www.fgodfrey.co.uk
Open: Mon-Fri 8am-6pm, Sat 8am-5pm **Closed:** Sun, Bank holidays **Tube:** Highbury & Islington **Bus:** 4, 19, 236
Payment: cash, cheque, Delta, Maestro, MasterCard, Visa
Bespoke local deliveries

This popular and well-established Quality Guild butcher places a huge emphasis on the origins of – and the methods used to farm – its meat and poultry. All of its produce is therefore free-range and additive and antibiotic free. Some is also organic, most notably the Kelly chicken, which has been declared the 'best in Britain' by a certain celebrity TV chef. Much of the shop's beef and lamb, including its lovingly prepared beef shin, is Orkney Island Gold. While the Godfreys concentrate on traditional butchery rather than innovation (you'll find beautifully trimmed pork rib chops and lamb racks, for instance, plus a full range of game including woodcock, wild rabbit and boar), they do offer a small selection of kitchen-ready marinated meats. Several of the shop's sausage lines have won industry gold and silver medals, and the number of top restaurants and hotels they supply is testament to the quality of their products and skills.

★ LA FROMAGERIE

Cheese shop

30 Highbury Park,
London N5 2AA
Tel/Fax: 020 7359 7440
Website: www.lafromagerie.co.uk
Open: Mon 10.30am-7.30pm, Tues-Fri 9.30am-7.30pm, Sat 9.30am-7pm, Sun 10am-5pm
Closed: Bank holidays, except the first one in May **Tube:** Highbury and Islington,

Arsenal **Bus:** 4, 19 **Mainline station:** Finsbury Park, Drayton Park **Payment:** cash, cheque, Amex, Delta, Electron, JCB, Maestro, MasterCard, Solo, Visa

Patricia Michelson's fabulous shop was recently – and deservedly – voted Best Independent Retailer in the *Observer Food Monthly*'s annual award. The accent here is, of course, on cheese, and a dedicated, cooled and humidified cheese room is packed full of handmade, artisanal cheeses. Their maturing process is overseen in the shop's basement by *affineur* Eric Demelle, who ensures that everything is wonderfully ripe. Be sure to try the Beaufort Chalet d'Alpage, the prince of French Gruyères; the Brie aux Truffes, which Michelson assembles herself; the mozzarella di bufala, supplied by a tiny producer based south of Naples; and the dense, unctuous Gorgonzola, which comes from a cheesemaker

based just south of Milan. The shop also carries directly sourced – and temptingly displayed – takeaway dishes, charcuterie, fresh produce, bread, chocolates, wines, tea and coffee. Many of these can be sampled at the Moxon Street branch's Tasting Café, which boasts a seasonal, daily-changing menu.

Branch: see Marylebone, page 39

Islington

★ CARLUCCIO'S

Italian
Delicatessen
Café

305-307 Upper Stret
London N1 2TU
Tel: 020 7359 8167

Main shop and branches: see Covent Garden, page 28

EUPHORIUM BAKERY

Bakery

202 Upper Street,
London N1 1RQ
Tel: 020 7704 6905
Order tel 020 7704 6905
Open: Mon-Thurs 7am-11pm,
Fri 7am-12am, Sat 8am-12am,
Sun 9am-11pm **Closed:** Bank
holidays, 25-27 Dec., 1 Jan.
Tube: Highbury & Islington **Bus:**
4, 19, 30, 43 **Mainline station:**
Highbury & Islington **Payment:**
cash, cheque, Amex, Delta,
Maestro, MasterCard, Visa
**Cakes to order, bespoke local
deliveries over £50**

Euphorium Bakery – an off-shoot of the successful Euphorium bar and restaurant – produces bread and pastries that are firmly rooted in the French and British tradition. The 15 bread lines include terrific baguettes, crusty British cobs and authentic Italian focaccia, made with '00' and semolina flours. (For most of the bread and cakes, the French pastry chef favours unbleached French flour and unsalted Dutch butter.) Savouries – all of which are pastry based – range from fashionable goat's cheese and pesto whirls to Cornish pasties. Sweet pastries include a full range of viennoiserie; large macaroons; Swiss rolls; buttery fruit tarts; St Honoré and simple, soured cream cheesecake; dark chocolate brownies; and moist Bramley apple and ginger tea cakes. There are also beautifully packaged jams, chutneys and bottled liqueur fruit, plus a growing sandwich range. All leftovers are given to the homeless at the end of each day.

Branch: 26A Chapel Market, London N1 9EN
Tel: 020 7837 7010

JAMES ELLIOTT, MASTER BUTCHER

96 Essex Road, London N1 8LU
Tel: 020 7226 3658
Open: Mon, Tues, Thurs 8am-5pm, Wed 10.30am-7pm, Fri 8am-7pm, Sat 7am-4pm **Closed:** Sun, Bank holidays **Tube:** Angel **Bus:** 38, 56, 73, 171a, 341 **Mainline station:** Essex Road **Payment:** cash, cheque

Butcher
Game dealer
Free range

Bespoke deliveries locally

With its old-fashioned window display crammed full of huge joints, whole carcasses and, in season, game birds in plumage, this excellent butcher is reassuringly traditional. All of the meat is guaranteed free-range and traceable. You'll find excellent beef, dry-cured, organic bacon, triple-smoked (over dry wood) gammon, home-cured salt brisket and a small range of home-made sausages, which includes, rather adventurously, a wild boar and apple variety. The farm-produced and mostly unpasteurized cheeses are chosen with great care. The selection includes Flower Marie, a soft ewe's milk cheese from Lewes, East Sussex, Isle of Mull Cheddar and James Aldridge's Somerset Tornegus. The shop also stocks plenty of good-quality pickles, chutneys, relishes and preserves.

MONTE'S

23 Canonbury Lane, London N1 2AS
Tel/Fax: 020 7354 4335
Open: Mon-Fri 10am-7pm, Sat 10am-6pm, Sun 10.30am-4pm
Closed: Bank holidays **Tube:** Highbury & Islington **Bus:** 4, 19, 30, 43 **Mainline station:** Highbury & Islington **Payment:** cash, cheque, Amex, Delta, Maestro, MasterCard, Visa
Bespoke deliveries locally, food-to-go, hampers

Italian
Delicatessen

This Italian delicatessen has a fresh, modern feel, with its shiny, steel shelving and shop-length chilled display. Brushed steel bowls are filled with colourful gift items including chocolate 'caviar' and 'sardines', and mini-*panettone*. Indeed, nothing of dull appearance would be granted any space here. The *fichi secchi*, *croccantini* and *teneri* are of the finest quality – and are also beautifully packaged. There is a fine range of olive oils and vinegars – check out the River Cafe's estate oils – and the wines, including Rocca Rubia, Copertino and Gavi di Gavil, have obviously been carefully chosen. You'll also find an abundance of salume and a good collection of cheeses. Pride of place in the chill cabinet goes to Julia Monte's home-made pasta, which comes in every imaginable colour. Look out for interesting sauces such as *rucola*, rose harissa and Siciliano, plus more traditional staples such as anchovies, breaded chicken escalopes and stuffed and bottled peppers. Colourful Illy coffee sets and a dramatic display of elegant grappas complete the picture.

NADELL PÂTISSERIE

French Pâtisserie

9 White Lion Street,
London N1 9HJ
Tel: 020 7833 2461
Fax: 020 7713 5036
Website:
www.nadellpatisserie.com
Open: Mon-Fri 9am-5pm
Closed: Sat, Sun, Bank holidays **Tube:** Angel **Bus:** 4, 30, 38, 73, 214, 274
Mainline station: Kings Cross **Payment:** cash, cheque
Bespoke delivery

This is very much a commercial enterprise, which mainly serves the trade. Pâtissier Michael Nadell and his team of artisans prepare all of the exquisite-looking cakes and tarts. Endorsements have come in the shape of seven gold and two silver medals awarded at various competitions in Frankfurt and England. The business even has a resident food technologist, Dr Helen Okello, who is responsible for quality assurance. To help you make up your mind, send for the pâtisserie's brochure, which includes more than 20 photographs, or take a look at its website. Most of the business is wholesale, but personal shoppers can choose from a selection of chocolate cakes, mousses, petits fours,

Neal's Yard Dairy

Borough branch – *see page 156*

Lisboa
Pâtisserie

Notting Hill – *see page 104*

tarts, flans and pastries. For a special occasion, try the pâtisserie's *croque-en-bouche*, which is beautifully decorated with sugar swans and flowers.

Bakery

RAAB'S BAKERS
136 Essex Road,
London N1 8LX
Tel: 020 7226 2830
Open: Mon-Sat 6am-6pm
Closed: Sun, Bank holidays
Tube: Angel **Bus:** 38, 56, 73, 341
Payment: cash, cheque

This traditional bakery is run by a Viennese family that has been in the business for generations. The premises look fairly unprepossessing at first, but on entering you will find a whole range of classic bread and cakes, all of which are baked on site every day. No animal fats or preservatives are used in any of the recipes, and the bread is baked in the traditional way, with the dough allowed to ferment for an hour before it is baked in a stone-floored oven. Choose from large wholemeal loaves, French sticks or Irish soda and sunflower seed bread, or try the speciality onion and walnut loaves. The cakes and buns – including old favourites such as iced fingers, Chelsea buns, Bakewell tarts, ginger biscuits and rock, Eccles and carrot cakes – are especially good. The bakery also has a takeaway counter, where

sandwiches are freshly prepared while you wait.

Italian Delicatessen

SAPONARA

23 Prebend Street,
London N1 8PF
Tel/Fax: 020 7226 2771
Open: Mon-Fri 8am-6pm, Sat 9am-6pm **Closed:** Sun, Bank holidays **Tube:** Angel **Bus:** 38, 56, 73, 171a, 271 **Mainline station:** Essex Road **Payment:** cash, cheque, Maestro
Bespoke deliveries locally

Set well back from Islington's main shopping drags of Essex Road and Upper Street, you will find this enticing little Italian deli, owned and run by Marco Saponara. Carefully selected and home-prepared produce, as well as a welcoming atmosphere, ensure a constant buzz. Saponara's greatest source of pride is the fresh pasta he has flown over twice a week from Italy: tagliatelle and plump ravioli with interesting fillings are joined by generously filled, tender *crespelle*. A good range of chef-made sauces, from *lucanica* to veal, via the more usual arrabbiata and bolognese, are available to accompany the pasta, as is Saponara's freshly pounded pesto. There is a good range of salumi, which includes *coppa di Parma*, *schiacciata piccante* and *salame al tartufo*. Truffles are very much in evidence in the cheese selection, too: three styles of truffled pecorino sit alongside rather fine Fontina, buffalo mozzarella and other staples. You'll also find fresh olives and antipasti, organic coffee, Italian wines and delightful sweetmeats including Maglio chocolates, luxuriously wrapped D'Amico 'Collezione' *panettone* and pastries. Saponara also offers freshly made, traditional panini.

★ STEVE HATT

Fishmonger

88-90 Essex Road,
London N1 8LU
Tel/Fax: 020 7226 3963
Open: Tues-Sat 7am-5pm
Closed: Sun, Mon, Bank holidays **Tube:** Angel **Bus:** 38, 56, 73, 171a, 341 **Mainline station:** Essex Road **Payment:** cash, cheque

Steve Hatt is in the fourth generation of his family to run this business, which is now well established as one of London's best fishmongers. He describes his driving force as a 'relentless

TINDERBOX

21 Upper Street, London N1 0PQ
Tel: 020 7354 8929

 In the Area This coffee bar on Islington's busy Upper Street is a firm favourite with locals, and rightly so. The staff knows how to make the perfect coffee, and the Matthew Algie beans are ground at cryogenic temperatures so that they don't 'burn'. If you're peckish, you can have a sandwich, pasta salad or a delicious cake. If coffee isn't your thing, try a fresh fruit smoothie, prepared to order. On Monday evenings, there is live music.

quest for quality' – and this is so palpable that it attracts custom from far and wide. Celebrity clientele alone (even admitting that Islington is singularly blessed with the species) is too numerous to list. You can expect to find a wide range of fish, including the finest wild sea bass and gilt-head bream. Everything is as fresh as can be: indeed, the tuna is sushi-class and the lobsters are live. There is plenty of seafood choice, too, including brown shrimps, raw prawns and Cornish crab sold in every which way. Smoked fish include exotic swordfish and halibut, while the haddock and mackerel are home-smoked. Festive specialities include everything from oscietra caviar to carp for Christmas, plus a full range of poultry and game to order. All of the usual adjuncts are here, too: look out for bottled *fonds*, squid ink and Perard fish soups.

Leytonstone

TURKISH FOOD CENTRE
647-661 High Road
London E11 4RD
Tel: 020 8558 8149

Main shop and branches: see Dalston, page 138

Newington Green

A HIGHER TASTE
47 Newington Green,
London N16 9PX

Tel/Fax: 020 7359 2338
Open: Mon-Sat 7.30am-9pm, Sun 9am-6pm **Closed:** Bank holidays **Mainline station:** Canonbury **Bus:** 73, 171a
Payment: cash, cheque
Food-to-go

This neighbourhood café offers fine vegetarian *traiteur* items, savouries, pastries and bread. Well-priced meze include idiosyncratically spelled humus, *tebule, cacik* and smoked aubergine. The olive- and tahini-flavoured bread, and the large selection of freshly made pastries with exotic names such as *Seker Pare, Lor Tay Lisi* and *Fistik Ezmesi* (translations, e.g. pistachio and marzipan for the latter, are preferred), are perhaps the best reasons to visit. You'll find genuine Turkish Delight, too.

ANTEPLILER
33 Green Lanes,
London N16 9BS
Tel: 020 7226 9409

Main shop: see Harringay, page 139

GALLO NERO DELICATESSEN
45 Newington Green Road,
London N1 4QT
Tel: 020 7226 2002

Main shop: see Stoke Newington, page 149

Turkish Food Hall

Turkish Delicatessen

Turkish Confectioner Pâtisserie

Italian Delicatessen

Turkish
Bakery
Pâtisserie

MANOR FARM BAKERY
108 Green Lanes,
London N16 9EH
Tel: 020 7254 7907
Open: Mon-Fri 9am-6.30pm
Closed: Sat, Sun, Bank holidays
Mainline station: Canonbury
Bus: 141, 171a **Payment:** cash

It's worth seeking out this little
shop, which, in spite of its rather
English-sounding name, is a
traditional Turkish bakery. The
quality and authenticity of the
bread are unsurpassed, and the
range includes well-made basics
(round, 'hatted' crusty loaves
and flat pittas), enriched dough
bread and a small selection of
savoury and sweet pastries.

Pentonville

Italian
Delicatessen
Greengrocer
Organic

OLGA STORES
30 Penton Street,
London N1 9XD
Tel: 020 7837 5467
Open: Mon-Fri 9am-8pm, Sat
9am-7pm, Sun 10am-2pm
Closed: Bank holidays **Tube:**
Angel **Bus:** 30, 73, 214 **Mainline
station:** King's Cross **Payment:**
cash, cheque, Delta, Maestro,
MasterCard, Visa

This small, friendly Italian
delicatessen also stocks a vast
array of Mediterranean produce.
At Christmas, it is packed with
festive bread and cakes – but
sweetmeats are something of a
year-round speciality, with
plenty of commercial and
artisan-produced Sicilian
pastries on display. Other

temptations include a wide range
of Jijonenca *turrone*, Spanish fig
cakes and chocolate-coated figs,
torroncini and Mulino Bianco
biscuits. You'll also find basics
such as oils, vinegars, pasta –
including, unusually, the
prestigious Cipriani varieties –
zampone, salume, tuna,
anchovies and clams in
abundance. Stuffed courgettes,
salsas, vegetarian croquettes and
ravioli stuffed with artichoke
and wild mushrooms are
popular. The shop also stocks
fresh fruit and vegetables, and a
decent range of wines.

Plaistow

TAWANA
243-245 Plaistow Road,
London E15 3EU
Tel: 020 8503 1639

Main shop: see Bayswater,
page 17

South-East
Asian
Grocer

South Woodford

JOSHUA HILL'S
126 George Lane,
London E18 1AD
Tel/Fax: 020 8989 3083
Open: Mon-Sat 7.30am-6pm
Closed: Sun, Bank holidays **Tube:**
South Woodford **Bus:** 179, 301,
549 **Payment:** cash, cheque,
Amex, Delta, Maestro,
MasterCard, Visa
Local deliveries, mail-order

Proprietor Graham Hill has built
up a reputation for his sausages
(250 varieties at last count, with

Sausages
Organic

50 are stocked at any one time) that is the envy of many London butchers. Indeed, European businessmen are known to hop on the tube and secret a cache of Hill's British bangers in their briefcases. To think of these paragons of excellence as British bangers is, perhaps, misleading. While it is no longer unusual to find that all ingredients are free-range or organic, it is rare to come across all-leg-meat pork sausages with no added fat. This recipe results in an increase in texture, density and flavour intensity, which is further boosted by the use of roughly chopped fresh herbs (Hill never uses dried) and inventive additions such as Normandy shallots, Dutch East India spice mix, whole lemon and hickory smoked pork. The majority of the sausages are gluten-free, and a purist's touch ensures that all ingredients in the organic range really are organic. The shop also functions as a deli – with beautifully displayed dips, sauces, anchovies, rollmops, pickles, olives, sweetmeats and chocolates on offer – and provides a catering service.

Stoke Newington

THE FISH CENTRE

Jewish Orthodox Fishmonger Kosher

8 Stamford Hill,
London N16 6XZ
Tel: 020 8442 4412
Fax: 020 8442 4754

Open: Tues-Thurs 8am-5pm, Fri 8am-1pm **Closed:** Sat, Sun, Mon, Jewish religious holidays
Mainline station: Stoke Newington **Bus:** 67, 76, 106, 149, 243 **Payment:** cash, cheque
Bespoke deliveries locally

This Jewish-run fishmonger is a narrow slip of a place, with a small display of glisteningly fresh fish. Shoppers are often startled to be served by fishmongers clad in black from head to toe; but despite such sombre appearance, service is always warm, humorous and helpful. Stock includes basics such as cod, haddock and pollock, plus plentiful supplies of fish that have special appeal to the Jewish community, such as salmon, salmon trout, bream and carp. Minced fish is apparently very popular with non-Jewish shoppers, as is the ready-to-cook rolled fish.

★ FRESH & WILD

32-40 Stoke Newington Church Street, London N16 0LU
Tel: 020 7254 2332

Food Hall
Organic

Main shop and branches: see Notting Hill, page 97

GALLO NERO DELICATESSEN

75 Stoke Newington High Street, London N16 8EL
Tel: 020 7254 9770
Open: Mon, Wed-Fri 8.30am-6.15pm, Tues 8.30am-2.15pm, Sat 8.30am-6pm **Closed:** Sun,

Italian
Delicatessen

Bank holidays **Mainline station:** Stoke Newington **Bus:** 67, 73, 76, 106, 149, 243 **Payment:** cash, cheque, Delta, Maestro, MasterCard, Visa

Both this shop and its branch in Newington Green have been established in the area for over 25 years, supplying 'everything Italian'. You'll find all of the basics: de Cecco, Agnesi and Molisana pasta, a variety of

risotto rice, and tins of tuna and anchovies, plus fine cheeses. The Moris produce their own, very popular pasta sauces and pestos, and the ham is home cooked. Home-made tiramisu panders to the Italian sweet tooth, as do the Italian ice creams and jars of rum *babas* and fruit in liqueur. Look out for treasures such as beautifully soft fillets of *baccala* (salt cod) and precious bottles of traditional Balsamic vinegar. A range of wines, spirits and coffee completes the picture.

Branch: see Newington Green, page 147

Green Street Market

Forest Gate, London E7
Open: Tues 8am-12pm, Thurs-Sat 8am-6pm **Tube:** Upton Park **Mainline station:** Forest Gate

This market is a mecca for anyone after keenly priced Asian, African and Caribbean ingredients. At Green Street Supermarket, you will find all sorts of Caribbean and Jamaican fresh fruit and veg, as well as groceries. The large daily covered market halfway down the road enjoys a bustling, cheerful atmosphere. Visit BB's Caribbean fishmongers for catfish, croaker and salt fish; or Toor Supermarket for huge bunches of fresh herbs, exotic African and Caribbean fruit and vegetables, and Indian and Bangladeshi beans of all shapes and sizes. Queues at the butchers are testament to the quality of the goat and mutton on sale.

Tottenham

★ LOON FUNG
111 Brantwood Road,
London N17 0DX
Tel: 020 8365 1132

Chinese
Food Hall

Main shop and branch: see Chinatown, page 27

TURKISH FOOD CENTRE
363 Fore Street,
London N9 0NR
Tel: 020 8807 6766

Turkish
Food Hall

542-544 Lordship Lane,
London N22 5BY
Tel: 020 8365 8846

678-682 High Road,
London N17 0AE
Tel: 020 8808 6664

Main shop and branches: see Dalston, page 138

Walthamstow Market

Walthamstow High Street
Open: Mon-Fri 9am-4pm, Sat 9am-5pm **Mainline station:** Walthamstow Central
Bus: 34, 97, 215, 357, W11

Not for nothing does this claim to be England's longest market. The stalls stretch for half a mile and occupy the length of the High Street all week, excluding Sunday, with over 500 pitches on Saturday, the busiest day. There are fruit and vegetable stalls galore, offering the usual variety at reasonable prices – though you can find more exotic produce from Asia and the Caribbean. There are also cheeses, sausage and shellfish stalls among the stands flogging old clothes, new clothes, household goods, furniture and records. The atmosphere is bustling and typically East End. If you're hungry, try a West Indian ready-made snack from a stall, or some pie and mash – or eels and mash – from the old-fashioned pie shops.

North Woolich Way

River Thames

A102(M) Motorway

Woolwich Rd

Charlton

Westcombe
Park

aze Hill

Charlton Rd

Little Heath

:ENWICH

CHARLTON

wich Park

rlton Way

OOTERS HILL RD

Shooters Hill Rd

KIDBROOKE

Tanquil Vale

heath

e Terrace

Kidbrooke

Well Hall Rd

Lee Rd

ACKHEATH

Rochester Way Relief Rd

Eltham

RD

Eltham Rd

r Green

Bernt Ash Rd

LEE

Eltham Hill

Lee

Westhorne Ave

Eltham

Court Rd

Baring Rd

Sidcup Rd

dure Lane

Mottingham

GROVE
PARK

Mottingham Rd

oot Lane

Grove Park Rd

Chinbrook Rd

Grove Park

Baring Rd

Burt Ash Rd

Elmstead
Woods

Hill

Coleg Rd

London Rd

Sund ridge Park

Weedy Rd

Bromley North

Widmore Rd

Shortlands

High St

Bickley Rd

BROMLEY

Bickley

Bromley South

South-East

Beckenham

Sausages

VILLAGERS SAUSAGES
91 The High Street,
Beckenham, Kent BR3 1AG
Tel/Fax: 020 8325 5475
Website:
www.englishsausages.com
Open: Mon-Sat 8.30am-5.30pm
Closed: Sun **Mainline station:**
Beckenham Junction **Bus:** 54,
276, 227 **Payment:** cash, cheque,
Amex, Delta, Maestro,
MasterCard, Visa
Mail order

This shop has an old-fashioned
approach to sausage making;
the staff eschews additives and
preservatives, and prepares
each and every sausage by hand.
With a selection of 65 varieties
always available, and up to 300
varieties available on request,
owner Ron Etheridge claims to
offer the largest selection of
bangers in the south of
England. Along with traditional
Cumberland and Lincolnshire
flavours, you will find venison,
wild boar and vegetarian spicy
cabbage varieties. The
international selection includes
vegetarian and gluten-free
offerings. Home-made pickles,
chutneys, sauces, fresh apple
juices and South African
biltong are also available,
along with prepared meat
dishes such as English leg of
lamb, which is boned and
stuffed with Toulouse
sausage meat.

Bermondsey

Food Hall

**LE PONT DE LA TOUR
FOODSTORE**
36D Shad Thames, Butler's
Wharf, London SE1 2YE
Tel: 020 7940 1830
Open: Mon-Fri 8am-8pm, Sat
and Sun 10am-6pm **Closed:** 25,
26 Dec. **Tube:** London Bridge
or Tower Hill **Bus:** 42, 47, 78,
188 **Mainline station:** London
Bridge **Payment:** cash, cheque,
Amex, Delta, Maestro,
MasterCard, Visa
Food-to-go

This is style guru and
ubiquitous restaurateur
Terence Conran's take on the
best-ever corner shop. Along
with the attractively packaged
groceries, there are plenty of
foods to take away, from filling
sandwiches made with loaves
baked daily on the premises, to
Italian antipasti, farmhouse
cheeses and top-quality
charcuterie. There is also an
outstanding selection of
poultry, meat, fish and game in
season. Everything is intended
to combine visual appeal with
top quality in this cornerstone
of Conran's riverside
Gastrodome complex. 'We
seek out the more unusual
products that not only taste
great but look fab in your
kitchen,' explains
a manager.

Blackheath

Delicatessen

HAND MADE FOOD
40 Tranquil Vale,
London SE3 OBD
Tel 020 8297 9966
Fax: 020 8265 5172
Open: Mon-Fri 9am-6pm, Sat 9am-5.30pm, Sun 9.30am-3.30pm **Closed:** Bank holidays
Mainline station: Blackheath **Bus:** 53, 54, 75,108 **Payment:** cash, cheque, Delta, Maestro, MasterCard, Visa
Food-to-go, catering, hampers

This high-quality, *traiteur*-style delicatessen is well kept and friendly. It offers a delicious and extensive range of ready-made starters, salads, main courses and puddings, all of which are cooked on the premises using organic and free-range meats and seasonal, organic vegetables. The dishes are not limited to traditional French fare; in fact, the owners describe themselves more as global cooks. They are widening the range of dishes all the time, and menus change with the seasons – so there is always something new to try. Choose from taramasalata made from Cornish cod's roe, chard and goat's curd puff pastry rolls, organic Irish salmon and herb fish cakes, and rhubarb, orange and apple crumble. They also produce their own pâtés and terrines and stock a good range of farmhouse cheeses, salamis, pasta, olive oils and sauces. It's always well worth a visit to stock up your fridge or freezer.

Borough

Fishmonger

★ ABERDEEN SEA PRODUCTS
Unit 2, Toulmin Street,
London SE1 1PP
Tel: 020 7407 0247
Fax: 020 7407 0248
Open: Mon-Fri 5.30am-12.30pm, Sat 5.30am-10am
Closed: Sun, Bank holidays **Tube:** Borough **Bus:** 35, 40, 133, 344, P3 **Mainline station:** London Bridge **Payment:** cash, cheque, Amex, MasterCard, Visa
Bespoke deliveries to Central/SE London (min order £30)

The first thing that is sure to strike a visitor to this essentially wholesale enterprise is the bareness of the warehouse-style entrance. The next impression is of a barely perceptible, sea-fresh smell and pristine cleanliness. You won't see much fish on display, though there's a constant buzz of activity and piles of boxes in the preparation room. A scan of the list, however, will tell you that almost anything can be found here, from cod to kingfish, prawns to Venus clams, smoked wild salmon and potted shrimps to caviar. Best bets, perhaps, are the Japanese sushi-grade salmon, sea bass, red snapper and tuna. Orders from restaurants flow thick and fast, and virtually all stock arrives straight from the coast and leaves the prep room on the same day, though a small quantity is kept frozen. You don't need to phone through for most varieties of fresh fish, though it is advisable if you're after exotics or seasonal shellfish.

Spanish
Delicatessen

★ BRINDISA
32 Borough Market
London SE1 9H
Tel: 020 7407 1036

Main shop: see Clerkenwell, page 60

Bakery
Organic

★ DE GUSTIBUS
5 Southwark Street,
London SE1 1TQ
Tel: 020 7407 3625

Main shop and branches: see Marylebone, page 36

Bakery
Pâtisserie

★ KONDITOR & COOK
10 Stoney Street,
London SE1 9AD
Tel: 020 7407 5100
Fax: 020 7407 5201
Website:
www.konditorandcook.com
Open: Mon-Fri 7.30am-6.30pm,
Sat 8.30am-2.30pm **Closed:** Sun,
Bank holidays **Tube and mainline
station:** London Bridge **Bus:** 17,
21, 35, 40, 43, 47, 48, 133, 141,
149, 343, 381, 521, RV1
Payment: cash, cheque, Amex,
Maestro, MasterCard, Visa
Bespoke wedding cakes

Only natural butter and free-range eggs are used in Konditor & Cook proprietor Gerhard Jenne's irresistible cakes, cookies and pastries – making this stylish bakery a favourite with actors from the nearby National Theatre and Old Vic. The reularly changing range of scrumptious baked goodies might include prune buns, plum tarts, whisky and orange *bombe* and 'magic' cakes. The wedding cakes have graced many high-society weddings. If you're in the mood for something less sweet, be sure to try the the delicious bread or the lunchtime snacks to take away.

Branches: see Bloomsbury, page 20, Soho, page 53, Waterloo, page 167

★ MONMOUTH COFFEE COMPANY
2 Park Street,
London SE1 9AB
Tel: 020 7645 3560

Coffee

Main shop: see Covent Garden, page 30

★ NEAL'S YARD DAIRY
6 Park Street,
London SE1 9AB
Tel: 020 74645 3554

Cheese shop

Main shop: see Covent Garden, page 31

Brixton

A & C CO.
3 Atlantic Road,
London SW8 8HX
Tel: 020 7733 3766
Open: Mon-Sat 8am-8pm
Closed: Sun **Tube:** Brixton **Bus:** 2,
3, 35, 41, 59, 109, 133, 196
Mainline station: Brixton

Delicatessen

Borough Market

Open: Thurs 12pm-6pm (limited range of traders), Fri 12pm-6pm, Sat 9am-4pm
Location: off Borough High Street, south side of London Bridge, close to Globe
Theatre and Tate Modern **Website:** www.boroughmarket.org.uk **Tube and mainline**
station: London Bridge **Bus:** 17, 21, 35, 40, 43, 47, 48, 133, 141, 149, 343, 381, 521, RV1

B orough Market dates back to Roman times and has been on the current site since the
late 18th century, though the current iron and glass superstructure is Victorian. It is
now the only wholesale and retail food market left in Central London. Towards the
weekend, the retailers take over (there are more than 70 stalls) and on Fridays and
Saturdays, the place is alive with crowds of food shoppers of all ages and nationalities.
You will find high-quality fishmongers, butchers, poultry and game dealers, bakers,
cheesemakers, delicatessens, greengrocers, wild mushroom specialists and much more.
Just as important as the retailers are the farm outlets, fishermen and fish smokers (e.g.
Wyndham Farm Poultry, Wild Beef, The Ginger Pig, Northfield Farm, Furness Fish and
Poultry, Shell Seekers, Brown & Forrest), the private cooks (e.g. Mrs Bassa's Indian
Kitchen, Scandelicious) and the specialist importers (e.g. Sardinia Organic, Cool Chile
Co). Whether you come here for some serious food shopping or simply to browse and
graze, it's a fantastic venue for quality and variety.

66 Mushrooms are natural fast food. Just fry quickly in
butter or olive oil with chopped garlic and seasoning.
A sprinkling of parsley turned through the pan just before
serving is all they need. 99

Alastair Hendy, food writer

Payment: cash, cheque

This delicatessen started life as
a Cypriot deli, but was taken
over 16 years ago by a friendly
Portuguese couple. They still
own it today, although it is run
by their equally charming son.
You'll find an eclectic mixture
of stock from Spain, Italy,
Portugal, Cyprus, Greece,
Poland and Brazil. Look out,
too, for delicious fresh filo,
olives, oils, Spanish and Italian
cheeses, chorizo, salami, bread
and dried pulses and pasta,
plus Italian biscuits and good,
fresh herbs.

Grocer
Greengrocer
Wholefoods
Organic

BRIXTON WHOLEFOODS
59 Atlantic Road,
London SW9 8HX
Tel: 020 7737 2210
Open: Mon 9.30am-7pm, Tues-Sat 9.30am-5.30pm **Closed:** Sun,
Bank holidays **Tube and mainline
station:** Brixton **Bus:** 2, 3, 35, 45,
109, 118, 133, 159, 196, 250
Payment: cash, cheque, Delta,
Maestro, MasterCard, Visa

Hillary Waterfield's health-food
shop is a popular spot near lively
Brixton Market. It's crammed
with organic fruit and veg, tea,
cheeses, butter, oils, Balsamic
vinegars, wines, rice, pasta and
pulses, as well as Rachel's
organic yoghurt and milk, and
Rocombe Farm ice cream.
Vegetarians and vegans will find
a range of tofu, soya chunks,
TVP, and GM-free and vegetable
sausage and burger mixes.
Sheep's milk, tempe, macrobiotic
products and gluten-free
vegetables are also available for
anyone on special diets. The
large, self-serve jars of more than
250 types of herbs and spices are
particularly popular with
regulars. Some of the more
unusual offerings include dried
nettles, hops, rosehips,
limeflower and bee pollen.

DELICATESSEN PIACENZA
2 Brixton Road,
London SW9 6BU
Tel: 020 7735 2121
Open: Mon-Sat 9am-7pm Sun
10am-4pm **Closed:** Bank
holidays **Tube:** Oval **Bus:** 3, 36,
109, 133, 159 **Mainline station:**
Elephant & Castle **Payment:**
cash, cheque

Italian
Delicatessen

Edoardo Coda and his family
have built up a friendly
neighbourhood delicatessen like
the ones you would expect to
find in his native Piacenza. The
shop stocks San Daniele ham,
along with a good selection of
salamis. The cheeses include
caccio ricotta (salted ricotta) and
salted mozzarella. Among the
specialities are Signora Coda's
home-made tortelloni with
vegetable stuffing, and a
selection of fresh pasta sauces.
You'll find familiar basil pesto,
as well as a red pesto with a hint
of chilli and Sicilian pesto with
almonds, sun-dried tomatoes
'and lots and lots of chillies and
garlic'. Just stir the cold sauces
into a pot of hot pasta and you
have the makings of an
authentic Italian meal. The
shelves are stocked with Italian
'00' flour for bread- and pizza-
making, plus de Cecco and
Emiliane dried pasta, and
freshly ground coffee. At
Christmas, the shop carries a
wide range of traditional
panettone.

Fishmonger

L. S. MASH AND SONS
11 Atlantic Road,
London SW9 8HX
Tel: 020 7274 6423
Open: Mon-Sat 7.30am-6pm
Closed: Sun, Bank holidays **Tube:** Brixton **Bus:** 2, 3, 35, 45, 109, 118, 133, 159, 196, 250 **Mainline station:** Brixton **Payment:** cash, cheque over £20

Lorne Mash is in the second generation of his family to run this friendly, neighbourhood shop catering for the local Caribbean and Portuguese communities. He claims to sell every kind of fish available. The seafood comes fresh daily from Billingsgate Market and the south coast, and includes West Indian and Portuguese favourites such as Jamaican snapper, talapia, red fish, octopus and salt fish. More conventional offerings include cod, mussels, trout and prawns.

Brixton Market

Electric Avenue, Brixton Station Road
Open: Mon, Tues and Thurs-Sat 8.30am-6pm, Wed 10am-3pm **Closed:** Bank holidays
Tube: Brixton **Bus:** 2, 3, 59, 133, 159, 196, 333, 432 **Mainline station:** Brixton

Between Brixton Road and Coldharbour Lane, a plethora of roads and covered arcades make up one of the most vibrant, ebullient and entertaining markets in the capital. Centred originally on Atlantic Road and Electric Avenue (so-called because it was one of the first shopping streets to be electrically lit), it is reputed to be the largest market in Europe for Caribbean and African foods, reflecting the needs of a large proportion of the locals – immigrants who settled the area in the late 1940s and early 1950s. Amid stalls of apples, tomatoes and potatoes, there are strikingly exotic displays of yams, okra, dried pulses, nuts, leaves, plantains and guavas. Butchers in the area specialize in offal and Halal meat; some offer mutton and goat. Fishmongers – of which there are several, principally in Granville Arcade – offer fish from all over the world, including croakers, snappers, tilapia, gleaming crabs and large, raw prawns. You'll also find bacon, spices, bread, old clothes, household goods, vinyl and wig shops and stalls. The atmosphere is electric, especially on Fridays and Saturdays, when the market is busiest: everyone is buying for the week ahead, bargains are being touted, jokes and gossip exchanged, and competing rhythms – calypso, jazz, reggae and gospel among them – thump from all sides.

159

Catford

Turkish
Food Hall
Halal

TURKISH FOOD CENTRE
163-165 Bromley Road,
London SE6 2NZ
Tel: 020 8698 9890

Main shop and branches: see
Dalston, page 138

Docklands

Chocolate

ACKERMANS
15 Cabot Square, Canary
Wharf, London E14 4QT
Tel: 020 7512 9113

Main shop: see Swiss Cottage,
page 134

Italian
Delicatessen
Café

★ CARLUCCIO'S
2 Nash Court, Canary Wharf,
London E14 5AG
Tel: 020 7719 1749

Main shop and branches: see
Covent Garden, page 28

Chocolate

MAXWELL & KENNEDY
Cabot Place West, Canary
Wharf, London E14 4QT
Tel: 020 7512 9113

Main shop: see City, page 59

Dulwich

Chocolate
Pâtisserie

AU CIEL
1A Calton Avenue,
London SE21 7DE
Tel/Fax: 020 8488 1111
Website: www.auciel.co.uk
Open: Mon-Sat 8.30am-5.30pm,
Sun 10am-5pm **Mainline station:**
North Dulwich **Bus:** P4, P13,

P15 **Payment:** cash, cheque,
Delta, Maestro, MasterCard,
Visa

Visiting this elegant, Provençal-
style chocolaterie/boulangerie is
a pleasure. Every element of the
shop, from the movable display-
panel stairwell storage to local
foundry-wrought cast-iron
chairs and glass-topped shelves
and tables, has been made with
aesthetics in mind. Thus the
Valrhona chocolates rest on
fluted, washed-clay dishes that
both prevent condensation and
display them to irresistible
perfection. The skills of the
proprietor, who is also an artist,
are evident in the chocolate
displays (look out for the
delicate 'cabbages', 'bunches of
grapes' and 'bouquets'),
wedding favours and custom-
made cakes. The latter are
hugely popular and can feed up
to 250 guests. Locals are also
particularly enamoured of the
full range of & Clarke's bread
(page 92) and the carefully
chosen selection of preserves,
which includes Ackermans
novelties (page 134), sugar-free
jams, glacé fruit and
Dartington's spiced cherries,
peaches, green figs and ginger.

THE CHEESE BLOCK
69 Lordship Lane,
London SE22 8EP
Tel: 020 8299 3636
Fax: 020 8694 2118
Open: Mon-Fri 9.30am-6.30pm,
Sat 9am-6pm **Closed:** Sun
Mainline station: East Dulwich

Cheese shop
Delicatessen

Fresh & Wild

Camden branch – *see page 115*

Previous page Chalmers & Gray

Notting Hill – *see page 95*

Billingsgate Fish Market

Open: Tues-Sat 5am-8.30am
Dockland Light Railway: West India Quay **Bus:** D6, D7, D8, 277

Billingsgate fish market moved to this modern warehouse location in 1982 from Lower Thames Street in the City, from where it had been trading for nearly a thousand years. The new market continues the great tradition of London's fish trade and still has a great atmosphere. If early mornings are not a problem for you, and you are after the best fish in London, this is the place to visit for an opportunity to see the largest selection of fish in the United Kingdom. Daily arrivals from the coast and overseas ensure fresh supplies and, with some 65 merchants trading in close proximity in the Market Hall, competition is keen. Every type of fish and seafood you can imagine is here, from white sturgeon and salted cod to Norwegian salmon and lobsters from Canada. Some of the traders are wholesale only, but many will do business with individuals, and it is certainly worth asking. In addition to the wide selection of fish and shellfish, you will also find stalls selling utensils and specialist catering supplies. If you want a bite to eat, there are two cafés on the premises.

Bus: 40, 176, 185 **Payment:** cash, cheque, Maestro, MasterCard, Visa

South Londoners flock to this wonderful shop, which stocks an average of 250 different cheeses – though, as Christmas approaches, the range increases to more than 300. With such a varied selection from the UK, France, Italy, Spain, Holland and Switzerland, there tends to be something for everyone. Look out for traditional farmhouse, organic and the increasingly difficult-to-find unpasteurized cheeses. The shop also stocks many products you would expect to find at any good deli, such as olives, pâtés, hams, salume, oils, vinegars, dried pasta, coffee and bread. Local produce includes lime pickle, honey from Dulwich Park and home-made organic bread. The filled rolls are also very popular.

★ EAST DULWICH DELI

15/17 Lordship Lane,
London SE22 8EW
Tel: 020 8693 2525
Fax: 020 8693 9444
Open: Mon–Sat 9am–6pm, Sun 10am–4pm
Bus: 40, 176, 185, P13
Mainline station: East Dulwich
Payment: cash, cheque, Amex, Delta, MasterCard, Maestro, Visa

Delicatessen
Grocer

This thriving delicatessen was born out of East Dulwich residents Tracey and Tony

Zoccola's frustration with the food offering – or lack thereof – in the area. 'We were tired of going to the West End to buy the nicer things that were missing here,' says Tracey. Since 2002, the couple has built a one-stop shop, where you can buy virtually everything you need to make a meal. The floor-to-ceiling shelves are crammed with top-quality products, including Colfiorito dried pasta, olive oils from the Zoccola family's estate just outside of Rome, Italian wines ranging in price from £6 to £100, Rococo chocolates (page 25) and Williamson & Magor tea. The deli counter is well stocked with popular desserts, including rich brownies and airy meringues prepared by the in-house kitchen. You'll also find Parmesan fresh from the wheel, plus home-cooked ham, a nice selection of seasonal, organic vegetables and bread from the Zoccola's own Born & Bread bakery, located on the Old Kent Road. Not content with running two successful enterprises, the couple is also looking to open another deli in Wandsworth, as well as a yoga centre/café/shop in East Dulwich.

Butcher
Game Dealer

HESTERS
126 Lordship Lane,
London SE22 8HD
Tel: 020 8693 9191
Open: Tues–Sat 7.30am–5.30pm
Closed: Sun, Mon **Bus:** 40, 176,
185, P13 **Mainline station:** East

Dulwich **Payment:** cash, cheque
Free delivery for orders over £20

Dave Isaac may be a newcomer to Dulwich, having only opened this popular butcher's shop in 2005, but he's been in the business for years. He owned and ran the eponymous butcher on Vauxhall's Kennington Lane for 20 years and also did a stint at Mayfair institution Allens Ltd (page 41). Hester's experience is evident in the top-quality cuts of meat and poultry that fill the shop's counters. You'll find melt-in-the-mouth Orkney beef and lamb, veal, duck, Balmoral and Royal Deeside venison, and – at Christmas – plump geese and Norfolk Black turkeys. A licensed dealer, Hester also stocks a range of game in season, including teal, grouse and pheasant. No matter how much you've been tempted into buying, don't leave the shop without some of the speciality sausages. Any one of the Cumberland, farmhouse pork, lamb merguez and gluten-free varieties makes for a fabulous Sunday-morning fry-up.

★ HOPE AND GREENWOOD
20 North Cross Road,
London SE22 9EU
Tel: 020 8613 1777
Website:
www.hopeandgreenwood.co.uk
Open: Mon–Sat 10am–6pm,
Sun 10am–5pm **Bus:** 40, 176,
185, P13 **Mainline station:** East
Dulwich **Payment:** cash, cheque,

Confectioners

It's good food and not fine words that keeps me alive.

Molière

Amex, Delta, Diner's Card, MasterCard, Maestro, Visa
Mail order

This is the sort of shop children dream about having on their street corners. Outside, a red-and-white striped awning flaps invitingly over a white picket fence and old-fashioned table and chairs. Inside, you'll find an impeccable evocation of a 1950s' sweet shop. Nat King Cole croons from the sound system, and the staff doles our quarters of sweets to children clutching imitation £5 and £10 ration books (an ingenious scheme introduced to help parents manage their children's sweet intake). They're spoilt for choice. The walls are lined with 175 glass jars filled with the likes of sweet tobacco, sherbet pips, lemon bonbons and floral gums – all painstakingly sourced from artisanal suppliers. Dishes laden with truffles, hunks of Hope and Greenwood's own range of chocolates, Victoria sponge and chocolate fudge cakes, and pick-and-mix fruit salad, Parma violets and candy teeth crowd the antique counter tops. Co-owner Kitty Hope has wanted to run a sweet shop since she

was small and, tapping into her previous career as a designer, has modelled Hope and Greenwood after her vision of Enid Blyton's *The Magic Faraway Tree*. It's a magical shop at any time, but drop by at Christmas, Easter and Halloween to see Hope's fabulous, seasonal window displays.

LA GASTRONOMIA

Italian Delicatessen

86 Park Hall Road,
London, SE21 8BW
Tel: 020 8766 0494
Open: Mon-Sat 9am-6pm
Closed: Sun, three weeks in the summer **Mainline station:** West Dulwich **Bus:** 3 **Payment:** cash, cheque, Amex, Delta, Maestro, MasterCard, Visa
Catering, food-to-go

Visiting this popular deli is like going to Italy without the hassle of international travel. You'll find savoury dishes, vegetable salads and cakes, all prepared daily. The affordable meals come ready-packed in microwaveable containers, which the friendly staff will heat up for you at lunchtime if you wish. You'll also find dried pasta, fresh bread, olive oils, charcuterie, meats and vegetable pâtés, grilled and marinated vegetables including olives and a selection of pasta sauces. The shop also sells 50 international cheeses. At Christmas, it is filled with up to 30 varieties of Italian biscuits, plus *panettone*, *pandoro* and *panforte*.

Branch: 135 Half Moon Lane, London SE24 9J
Tel: 020 7274 1034

Greengrocer
Wholefoods
Organic

SMBS FOODS
75 Lordship Lane,
London SE22 8EP
Tel: 020 8693 7792
Open: Mon-Fri 9am-6.30pm, Sat 9am-6pm, Sun 10am-5pm
Closed: Bank holidays Mainline station: East Dulwich Bus: 12, 40, 176, 185, 312 Payment: cash, cheque, Delta, Maestro, MasterCard, Visa

This shop, an eclectic treasure trove of high-quality foods, is owned by the same people who own the better-known Cheese Block (page 160) and is located just a couple of doors down the road from it. The outdoor display of seasonal fruit and vegetables is accessible enough, but beyond that you will have to hunt a little along a couple of high-stacked and somewhat narrow passageways to find whatever you are seeking. This might be anything from organic and artisanal bread, biscuits, baby foods, dairy produce, and fresh and frozen meats, to any number of ethnic foods (look

out for salt cod, plantain crackers, preserved black beans, palm sugar, fresh lime leaves, lemongrass and *umeboshi*) and spices, no matter how abstruse. Grains include the likes of biodynamic risotto rice, freekeh, quinoa and Hopi blue popping corn. Bakers will appreciate the almond oil, rosewater, fresh organic yeast, and Himalayan lotus and wildflower honey. The healthily self-indulgent can choose from a wide range of organic ices from Yeo Valley, Green & Black, Rocombe Farm, Swedish Glace and Hill Station. There is also a fantastic selection of gluten-, wheat- and dairy-free products for those with special dietary needs.

Elephant & Castle

LA BODEGUITA
Unit 256, Upper Level,
Elephant & Castle Shopping Centre, London SE1 6TE
Tel/Fax: 020 7708 5826
Website: www.labodeguita.co.uk
Open: Mon-Sat 8.30am-8pm
Closed: Sun, Bank holidays Tube and mainline station: Elephant & Castle Bus: 1, 12, 35, 45, 53, 63, 68, 168, 171, 176, 188, 344, C10
Payment: cash
Food-to-go, mail order

Columbian
Grocer

This café-cum-kiosk, located in the somewhat bleak setting of the Elephant & Castle Shopping Centre, is a popular gathering spot for the local Latin American community – though it is also of

Greenwich Market

Off Stockwell Street
Open: Sat, Sun 9.30am-5.30pm **Mainline station:** Greenwich
Bus: 53, 53X, 177, 180, 188, 199, 286, 386

A visit to Greenwich deserves at least a day: there is the National Maritime Museum, the Greenwich Observatory, the Cutty Sark – and the markets. Sunday is the most popular day for the latter, which offer antiques, bric-à-brac, crafts, books, and new and old clothes in a variety of locations, both under cover and in the open air. Saturday, though, is the day to go for food. By the side of the Village Market, off Stockwell Street, some half dozen or so traders offer organic foods including olives, olive oils, eggs, cheeses, bread, meats, sausages, fruit and vegetables.

considerable interest to anyone seeking out authentic Colombian ingredients. These include PAN maize flour, *yuca harina* (tapioca starch), pastry and *buñuelos* mixes, *frijoles*, chocolate to grind for drinks and cooking, *panella* molasses and preserved figs. Equally fascinating is the ever-changing range of home-cooked foods to eat on the spot or take away. This includes *Cuchuco de trigo, Aborrajados*, Colombian *Empanadas* and *Queso* (cheesecake). Enjoy a cup of the shop's outstanding coffee while you browse.

Greenwich

THE CHEESEBOARD
26 Royal Hill,
London SE10 8RT
Tel: 020 8305 0401
Website:
www.cheese-board.co.uk
Open: Mon-Wed and Sat 9am-5pm, Thurs 9am-1pm, Fri 9am-5.30pm **Closed:** Sun **Mainline station:** Greenwich **Bus:** 53, 53X, 180, 199 **Payment:** cash, cheque, Amex, Delta, Maestro, MasterCard, Visa
Free local delivery on orders over £20, mail-order

This pretty corner shop is the first in a charming row of little shops with old frontages

Cheese shop

situated just outside the main throb of Greenwich centre. It offers a range of more than 150 cheeses from all over Europe and specializes in farmhouse cheeses, many of which are unpasteurized. The cheeses range from the classic English farmhouse Stiltons, Caerphilly and Cheddars to more unusual Spanish cheeses, high-quality mozzarellas and a vast selection of French cheeses such as St Agur, Vignotte and wonderful goat's cheeses. Over the years, the shop has built up an excellent reputation and a solid clientele. It also sells freshly baked bread including French and Italian loaves, Jewish bagels and chollas, plus other speciality bread from & Clarke's (page 92). Cheese-related foods on offer include chutneys, mustards, pickles, biscuits, ports, wines and champagnes. Regular cheese tastings are held, and the shop also caters for corporate events.

Butcher
Sausages
Organic

DRINGS

22 Royal Hill,
London SE10 8RT
Tel: 020 8858 4032
Open: Mon-Sat 8am-5pm, Thurs 8am-1pm **Closed:** Sun **Mainline station:** Greenwich **Bus:** 53, 53X, 180, 199 **Payment:** cash, cheque

Established in 1910, this is one of London's few remaining traditional family butchers (there's even sawdust on the floor). The Dring brothers, David and Robert, offer friendly, personal service; they seem to

know most of the customers by name and claim that, between them, there is nothing they don't know about meat. There's a wide selection of high-quality meat on offer, but the sausages are the real draw. You'll also find organic and free-range chicken, as well as organic pork. Anything unusual can be ordered in advance, and the Drings will cut meat to any specification.

Herne Hill

MIMOSA

Delicatessen

16 Half Moon Lane,
London SE24 9HU
Tel: 020 7733 8838
Fax: 020 7733 9803
Open: Mon-Fri 9am-7pm, Sat 9am-5.30pm, Sun 9am-3pm
Mainline station: Herne Hill **Bus:** 37 **Payment:** cash, cheque, Delta, Maestro, MasterCard, Visa
Catering, food-to-go

This popular *traiteur* is renowned for its wonderful French, Moroccan and Mediterraean dishes. Brochettes of Moroccan marinated chicken and a daily selection of freshly made quiches are among the

temptations, but the shop is best known for its houmous (the staff makes 250 kilos a year), roasted aubergine dip, Moroccan pepper relish and couscous salad. You'll also find French desserts – be sure to try the crème brûlée, fruit tarts and meringues – and French and English cheeses including Montgomery and Keen's Cheddars and Colston Bassett Stilton. Look out, too, for the fine selection of smoked and cooked French hams, Spanish chorizos, Italian salamis, French chocolates, handmade Belgian truffles and superb wines and champagnes. When the weather cooperates, enjoy a pastry or lunch in the shop's garden patio.

Lewisham

Turkish
Food Hall
Halal

TURKISH FOOD CENTRE
227-229 Lewisham High Street,
London SE13 6LY
Tel: 020 8318 0436

Main shop and branches: see
Dalston, page 138

Waterloo

Bakery
Pâtisserie

★ KONDITOR & COOK
22 Cornwall Road,
London SE1 8TW
Tel: 020 7261 0456

Main shop and branches: see
Borough, page 156

West Norwood

**WEST NORWOOD
FISHMONGERS**
326 Norwood Road,
London SE27 9AF
Tel: 020 8670 0880
Website:
www.thescuttlefish.co.uk
Open: Tues-Sat 9am-5pm **Closed:**
Sun **Mainline station:** West
Norwood **Bus:** 2, 68, X68
Payment: cash, cheque
Mail order

Fishmonger

This fishmonger may look unassuming, but its proprietor, Paul Ayers, makes it a point to stock only the best-quality fish that can be found in the market each day. Tuna loin is popular, as are the giant, fresh prawns sold in their shells. Swordfish and scallops are also favourites during the summer months. Freshly smoked fish is a speciality and comes from the shop's own traditional smokehouse at the back of the premises. Smoked, undyed haddock and kippers are on offer, as is tempting smoked rainbow trout. Wild salmon is available in season, and orders are accepted. With friendly service besides, this shop is well worth a visit.

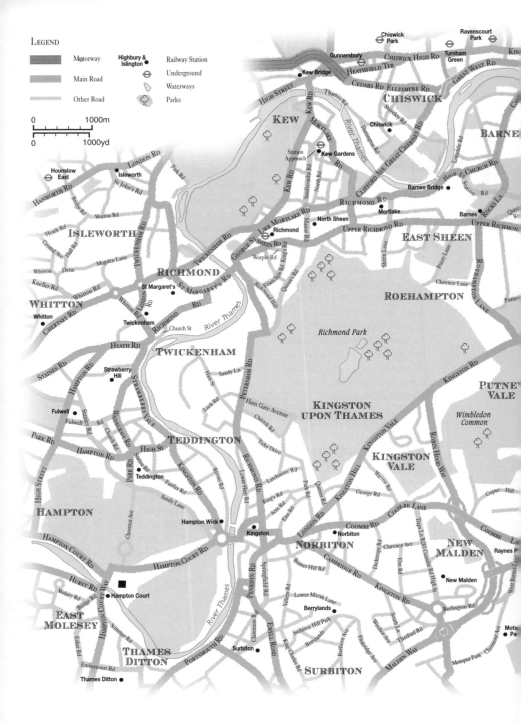

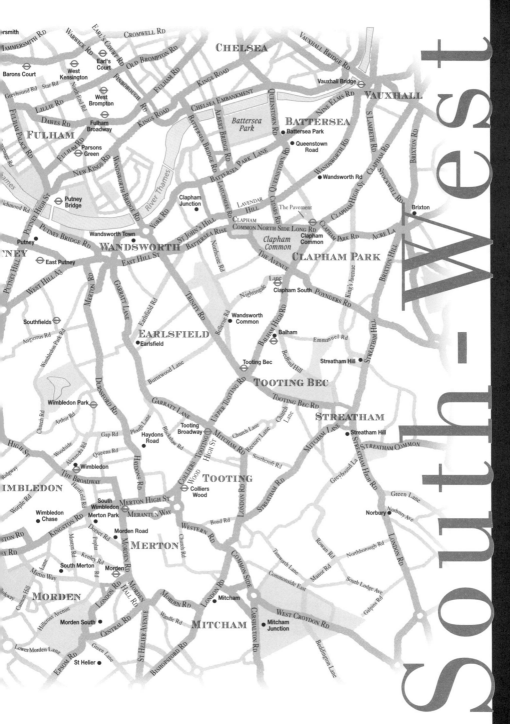

Barnes

Fishmonger

ALEXANDER & KNIGHT

18 High Street,
London SW13 9LW
Tel: 020 8876 1297
Open: Tues and Thurs-Sat 8am-5pm, Wed 8am-4pm **Closed:** Mon, Sun, Bank holidays
Mainline station: Barnes Bridge
Bus: 33, R69, 209 **Payment:** cash, cheque, Amex, Delta, Maestro, MasterCard, Visa
Food-to-go

This friendly fishmonger, run by Chris Lofthouse, is one of the several high-quality shops situated along the high street. Lofthouse has been here since 1984, and his range of farmed and wild seafood is impressive, whether you're after some mackerel or haddock for a family supper, or dinner-party fare such as black bream, loin of tuna, cod for roasting or tiger prawns. There is a great range of smoked fish, including organic salmon, cod's roe, eel fillets and mackerel. The shop's bass is from Newlyn, its herrings from Orkney and its oysters from Ireland. Cockles and clams are available in season, and occasionally you'll find the more unusual razor-shell clams and sea urchins. When you don't want to cook, try the salmon fish cakes, dressed crabs or a jar of French fish soup.

★ GUSTO AND RELISH

56 White Hart Lane,
London SW13 0PZ
Tel: 020 8878 2005
Open: Mon-Fri 10am-7pm, Sat 10am-6pm, Sun 9am-1pm
Closed: Sun in August
Mainline station: Barnes Bridge
Bus: 33, R69, 209 **Payment:** cash, cheque, Delta, Maestro, MasterCard, Visa
Catering, food-to-go, hampers

This imaginatively stocked *traiteur*/deli, run by former restaurant owners Sally O'Gorman and Richard Lane, sells a wide range of fresh food-to-go, Continental groceries and a quirky selection of wines from south-west France. O'Gorman prepares all of the scrumptious takeaway dishes – which might include winter stews, game pies, fish cakes, stuffed peppers, lemon roulade, tarte tatin and fresh cheesecake – on the premises. She and her partner are passionate about what they do and generous with their knowledge. Among the groceries and deli items, you'll

Traiteur
Delicatessen

WORTH A DETOUR

The Dining Room Shop, 62-64 White Hart Lane,
Tel: 020 8878 1020
Crockery, cutlery, glassware.
Tobias and the Angel, 66 White Hart Lane,
Tel: 020 8296 0058
Unusual antique kitchenware and household goods.
The Blue Door, 74 Church Road,
Tel: 020 8748 9785
Swedish hand-made home and dining accessories.

find Neal's Yard Dairy cheeses (page 31) including Doddington, Harbourne Blue, Mrs Kirkham's Lancashire, Cashel Blue and Seaton's Orkney varieties, plus a selection of French, Italian and Spanish cheeses supplied by La Fromagerie (page 141). There is also a wide range of artisanal bread, and the home-made pesto, coriander paste, tapenade and chilli-hot harissa (authentically scented with rose petals) make good bases for sauces and dips. Charcuterie includes pâtés and terrines, cured hams from Italy and Spain (San Daniele and *jamon Serrano*), Spanish sausages (*lomo de Teruel, Leon salchiccon* and Catalan chorizo), *felinetto* and chilli-flavoured salume. O'Gorman and Lane have also sourced a wide range of preserves and bottled sauces, plus interesting pasta, Vialone Nano risotto rice, Calasparra paella rice and polenta flour. Richard Woodall's dry-cured bacon and Forman's smoked salmon can be found in the fridge alongside salad leaves and Neal's Yard Dairy products (page 31).

J. SEAL BUTCHERS

7 High Street,
London SW13 9LW
Tel: 020 8876 5118
Open: Mon and Tues, Thurs and Fri 7am-5.30pm, Wed 7am-1pm, Sat 6.30am-4pm **Closed:** Sun, Bank holidays **Mainline station:** Barnes Bridge **Bus:** 33,

R69, 209 **Payment:** cash, cheque, Delta, Maestro, MasterCard, Visa

An ox-blood red exterior greets you when you visit this family-run, old-fashioned butcher and delicatessen. There has been a butcher's shop on this site since 1850, and the Harrison family has been at the helm for more than 40 years, with a son now training to take over. The shop sells excellent beef, grass-fed lamb from Dorset, free-range pork from Suffolk, free-range chickens, game in season and organic turkeys and geese at Christmas (expect long queues). The staff will also prepare crown roasts and guards of honour to order. You'll also find a fine selection of cooked pies from The Real Pie Co., including steak and kidney, and vegetarian leek and potato options.

SONNY'S FOOD SHOP

92 Church Road,
London SW13 0DQ
Tel: 020 8741 8451
Fax: 020 8748 2698
Open: Mon-Sat 10am-6pm **Tube:** Hammersmith **Bus:** 9, 209, 33, 72 **Mainline station:** Barnes
Payment: cash, cheque, Delta, MasterCard, Visa
Catering, food-to-go

Situated next door to the restaurant of the same name is this busy little delicatessen, crammed with goodies from France and Italy. Machiavelli's

French
Italian
Delicatessen

fresh, handmade pasta is flown in twice a week from Italy, and you can also order *vincisgrassi*, a white lasagne made from truffles, *ceps* and Parma ham, voted the Best Lasagne in the World by Charles Campion of the *Evening Standard*. You'll also find devilishly good chocolates from Norwood House and The Chocolate Society (page 18), a selection of Poilâne bread (page 19) and delicious, award-winning cakes, organic bread and muffins – the date and walnut loaf is particularly good. There are fine preserves including own-label marmalades, jams and pickles, plus high-quality olive oils and vinegars. The shop's takeaway dishes, which are freshly prepared on the premises, are outstanding. A typical selection might include a casserole of the day, poached chicken supreme, stuffed Piedmontese peppers, potato and onion tortilla, chargrilled vegetables, salmon fish cakes and herbed couscous.

Greengrocer
Organic

TWO PEAS IN A POD
85 Church Road,
London SW13 9HH
Tel/Fax: 020 8748 0232
Open: Mon-Sat 8am-5.30pm,
Sun 10am-1pm **Closed:** Bank
holidays **Mainline station:** Barnes
Bridge **Bus:** 209 **Payment:** cash
Free local delivery

This tiny shop can get crowded, but is always worth a visit for its excellent produce. Fruit and vegetables from all over the world include plenty of seasonal British produce, herbs from the Channel Islands and soft fruit from Scotland. 'The whole world is going organic', says proprietor Malcolm Louis, 'and look: everything's getting dirtier!' Sure enough, the shop's unevenly shaped, earth-covered organic potatoes and carrots look how vegetables always used to look. Two Peas in a Pod enjoys a loyal customer base – the staff is on first-name terms with many of them – which might have something to do with its commitment to good service. 'If you can't see it in the shop, we'll get it in for you straightaway,' says Louis.

Battersea

COPE'S SEAFOOD
46 Northcote Road,
London SW11 1NZ
Tel: 020 7371 7300

Fishmonger

Main shop: see Fulham, page 82

DOVES
71 Northcote Road,
London SW11 6PJ
Tel: 020 7223 5191
Fax: 020 7801 0627
Open: Mon 8am-4pm, Tues-Sat
8am-5.30pm **Closed:** Sun, Bank
holidays **Tube:** Clapham South
Bus: 319, G1 **Mainline station:**
Clapham Junction **Payment:**
cash, cheque, Delta, Maestro,
MasterCard, Visa
Free local delivery
This well-established local butcher has been in business

Butcher
Pies

since 1889 and now specializes in free-range and organic meats – particularly Aberdeen Angus and Highland beef, grass-fed Welsh lamb, cooked ham, sausages and, at Christmas, the much sought-after bronze turkeys. Also popular – especially with dinner-party hostesses who are short on time – are the pies baked each day by the owner's wife. All are made without preservatives or colouring. Varieties include steak and claret, steak in Guinness, venison in cider and chicken, and ham and leek in a creamy tarragon sauce.

Organic Grocer

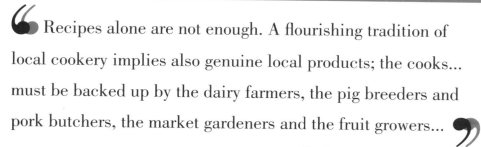

★ FRESH & WILD
305-311 Lavender Hill,
London SW11 1LN
Tel: 020 7585 1488

Main shop and branches: see
Notting Hill, page 97

French Bakery Delicatessen

GATEAUX DE MARIAGE
12 Queens Town Road,
London SW8 3RX
Tel: 020 7720 4844

Fax: 020 8674 6086
Website:
www.gateauxdemariage.co.uk
Open: Mon-Sat 9am-6pm **Closed:**
Sun **Tube:** Clapham Common
Bus: 137 **Mainline station:**
Battersea Park, Queenstown
Road **Payment:** cash, cheque,
Amex, Maestro, MasterCard,
Visa
Catering, food-to-go, mail order

This French *traiteur*/delicatessen offers a genuine taste of France. Inside, there is a wonderful smell of fresh bread, as all baguettes are baked on the premises. You can also buy everything you need for lunch, an evening meal or a special dinner party, from bread to cheeses to ready-made dishes such as salads, cassoulets, pizzas and quiches. The shop's speciality, however, is its exquisite cakes. French pastry chef Jean-Marc Fouque, formerly head pastry chef at Claridge's and executive chef for Maison Blanc in Oxford, designs traditional and

> ❝ Recipes alone are not enough. A flourishing tradition of local cookery implies also genuine local products; the cooks... must be backed up by the dairy farmers, the pig breeders and pork butchers, the market gardeners and the fruit growers... ❞
>
> Elizabeth David

modern wedding, party and celebration cakes including the popular *croque en bouche*, a pyramid of choux buns drizzled with caramel.

Cheese shop
Delicatessen

HAMISH JOHNSTON

48 Northcote Road,
London SW11 1PA
Tel: 020 7738 0741
Open: Mon-Sat 9am-6pm
Closed: Sun **Tube:** Clapham
Common **Bus:** 319, G1 **Mainline
station:** Clapham Junction
Payment: cash, cheque, Delta,
Maestro, MasterCard, Visa
Free local delivery, mail order

This fine cheese shop specializes in products sourced from artisanal producers. It carries more than 120 British, Irish, French, Spanish and Italian farmhouse cheeses, with wonderful names such as vintage Lincolnshire Poacher and Cropwell Bishop Stilton. In addition, you'll find a good range of smoked fish from the Summer Isles smokehouse in Achiltibuie, as well as bacon and dry-cured ham from the whey-fed pigs of Denhay Farm. Bowls brim with fresh olives, and there are huge flagons of olive oils from Italy, California, France and Spain from which you can fill your own container. Look out for the excellent pickles, relishes, mustards, speciality bread and biscuits, and some wonderful fudge from The Toffee Shop at Penrith.

THE HIVE HONEY SHOP

93 Northcote Road,
London SW11 6PL
Tel: 020 7924 6233
Website:
www.thehivehoneyshop.co.uk
Open: Mon-Sat 10am-5pm
Closed: Sun **Tube:** Clapham
Common **Bus:** 319, G1 **Mainline
station:** Clapham Junction
Payment: cash, cheque, Delta,
MasterCard, Visa
Mail order

This small shop probably has the largest selection of honeys and honey products in London – plus an incredible, five-foot-high, glass-fronted working hive of 20,000 bees. The honeys produced from the beekeeper owner's own hives, which are dotted around the country but are mostly in London, are the main attraction. He creates an excellent range of exclusive, single flower honeys that includes limetree, hawthorne and *sainfoin* varieties flavoured with ginger, raisin, and cognac and rum. You'll also find candles, cosmetics, mustards, and cough and cold cures. Bee-keeping equipment and books are available, and the owner also runs regular bee-keeping courses.

Honey

Italian
Traiteur
Delicatessen

★ I SAPORI DI STEFANO CAVALLINI

146 Northcote Road,
London SW11 6RD
Tel: 020 7228 2017
Fax: 020 7223 3859
Open: Mon-Fri 9.30am-7pm, Sat 9.30am-6.30pm **Closed:** Sun
Bus: 319, G1 **Mainline station:** Clapham Common **Payment:** cash, cheque, Delta, MasterCard, Maestro, Visa
Catering, desserts to order, free delivery (for orders over £50)

Michelin-starred chef Stefano Cavallini occasionally laments setting up shop at the quieter end of Northcote Road, but its location hasn't stopped London's gastronomes and homesick Italians from seeking out this superb *traiteur* and delicatessen. You'll find everything you need to stock an authentic Italian kitchen here. Latini dried pasta, Mulino Bianco crackers and biscuits, olive oils, wines, handmade Italian chocolates and a selection of ice creams from Acton-based artisanal gelateria AlbaGold are among the temptations. Cavallini has handpicked each item and is equally hands-on when it comes to the cheeses, meats and pasta. He won't stock dolcelatte – which he doesn't rate – but as recompense has sourced gorgeous pecorino sardo, Fontina and Bastardo cheeses. The meat counter includes similarly enticing bresaola, pancetta and chargrilled ham. Cavallini makes the popular ravioli by hand every day, but leaves the preparation of pasta dishes, sauces, salads and desserts to his excellent in-house chef. Just try to leave empty-handed.

 And the only reason for making honey

is so I can eat it.   Winnie-the-Pooh

Northcote Road Market

Open: Mon-Sat 7am-6.15pm
Tube: Clapham Common **Bus:** 319, G1
Mainline station: Clapham Junction

This excellent local market lines one side of Northcote Road – which has become rather foodie in orientation – as it bisects Battersea Rise. Most of the 30 or so stalls specialize in fresh fruit and vegetables, some of which is everyday stuff, but there are a lot of Afro-Caribbean lines as well. It is busier and more atmospheric on Saturdays, when there is also a French market.

inside the door, you'll find a selection of fresh bread and cakes from suppliers such as Neal's Yard Bakery and Crayve's, which produces wheat- and gluten-free baked goods. There is also a *traiteur* section at the front where chef Ian Loynes produces a daily-changing menu of tempting soups, salads, handmade pasta, pâtés, cakes and pastries. Dishes include the likes of lasagna, cream of carrot and chive soup, espresso and hazelnut brownies, and chocolate and cardamom cake. The shop also has an impressive selection of organic products, including Luscombe ginger beer, Kinvara smoked salmon, Simply Organic soups, Truuuly Scrumptious baby foods and a range of wholewheat pasta and flours. You'll also find a good range of frozen ready-meals.

Organic
Delicatessen

KELLY'S ORGANIC FOODS
46 Northcote Road,
London SW11 1NZ
Tel/Fax: 020 7207 3967
Open: Mon-Thurs 9am-8pm, Fri-Sat 9am-6pm **Closed:** Sun, Bank holidays **Tube:** Clapham South
Bus: 319, G1 **Mainline station:** Clapham Junction
Payment: cash, cheque, Amex, Delta, Maestro, MasterCard, Visa
Catering, food-to-go

Daniel Kelly owns and runs this totally organic delicatessen. Fresh fruit and vegetables are piled up in the window and, just

★ LIGHTHOUSE BAKERY
64 Northcote Road,
London SW11 6QL
Tel: 020 7228 4537
Website:
www.lighthousebakery.co.uk
Open: Tues-Sat 8.30am-5pm
Closed: Sun, Mon
Bus: 319, G1 **Mainline station:** Clapham Junction **Payment:** cash, cheque, Delta, Maestro, MasterCard, Visa
Bread, cakes and tarts to order

Since opening in 2000, this charming bakery has become an integral part of local life. An endless stream of mums and

Bakery

LA CUISINIÈRE
81-83 and 91 Northcote Road, London
SW11 6PJ **Tel:** 020 7223 4487

In the Area These two friendly shops sell everything you could possibly need for cooking and dining, including cutlery, classic French and Portuguese crockery, pots, utensils, baskets, picnic and barbecue ware, and more unusual items such as pre-packed picnic back-packs and titanium pots. Helpful and friendly staff are on hand to offer advice.

small children – most of whom co-owners Rachel Duffield and Elizabeth Weisberg know by name – drop by for freshly baked artisanal loaves and after-dinner treats. 'We wanted to create a local baker with a sense of community. It was important to us to produce good-quality bread using traditional methods – but not at boutique prices,' notes Duffield. You'll almost always find the popular traditional English farmhouse and stone-ground wholemeal loaves here, but the inventive Duffield and Weisberg mix up their other offerings with the seasons and 'as the whim takes them'. On any given day, you might find bagels, bialys or loaves of English sourdough or black Russian bread. And the pastries and 'sweet things' counter could include anything fron traditional Jewish hammentaschen (tri-cornered buttery cookies with purée plum filling) and colourful Carnival doughnuts to raspberry and white chocolate muffins or a selection of gingerbread critters. The only constant is that everything is baked using flours from Shipton Mill and Cann Mill – and all of the sandwiches' and baked goods' fillings come from nearby Hamish Johnston (page 174), Doves (page 172) and the fruit-and-vegetable stand outside the bakery. A visit at any time is a treat, but go on Saturday, when up to 35 different types of speciality bread are available, for something a bit special.

MISE-EN-PLACE
21 Battersea Rise,
London SW11 1HG
Tel: 020 7228 4392
Fax: 020 7924 1911
Open: Mon-Sun
8am-8pm **Closed:** Bank
holidays **Tube:** Clapham
Common **Bus:** 35, 37
Mainline station:
Clapham Junction
Payment: cash, cheque,
Delta, Maestro,
MasterCard, Visa
Catering, food-to-go

Delicatessen

The staff is helpful and friendly at this thriving shop, and the fresh food counters positively groan with mainly French and Italian goodies. There is plenty of organic food on offer here, but the emphasis is more on fresh ingredients sourced from reliable suppliers. Among the enticements, you'll find Poilâne bread (page 19), free-range goose eggs and Spanish Trevelez ham, which is air-dried in the mountains of Sierra Nevada for a minimum of 20 months. The cheeses are mostly English, French and Italian, while the ready-prepared foods include home-made pestos and sauces, pies, quiches and salads. The shelves are stacked with oils, vinegars, chutneys, preserves, biscuits and dried pasta, and the coffee shop at the back is popular with browsing shoppers.

Italian
Delicatessen

SALUMERIA NAPOLI

69 Northcote Road,
London SW11 1NP
Tel: 020 7228 2445
Open: Mon-Sat 9am-6pm
Closed: Sun, Bank holidays
Mainline station: Clapham
Junction **Bus:** G1, 319 **Payment:** cash, cheque

This authentic Italian delicatessen is a real find, as the owner, Salvatore Maggiulli, imports most of his Italian products directly. As well as a good selection of Italian biscuits, olives and pasta sauces, you'll find a choice of regional olive oils, including some organic ones, and every shape of dried pasta you can imagine. The bread – including focaccia, ciabatta and *casareccio toscano* – is supplied daily by Sicilian bakers, and the tortelloni and four varieties of home-made pesto are freshly prepared each day.

Clapham

Delicatessen

BON VIVANT DELICATESSEN

59 Nightingale Lane,
London SW12 8ST
Tel: 020 8675 6314
Open: Mon-Fri 8.30am-8pm,
Sat 8.30am-7pm, Sun 9.30-
12.30pm; open on occasional
Bank holidays **Closed:** 25, 26,
Dec., 1 Jan. and sometimes
other days between Christmas
and New Year **Tube:** Clapham
South **Bus:** 319, G1 **Payment:**
cash, cheque, Delta, Maestro,
MasterCard, Visa

This friendly local deli, run by Rachel Husband, has a distinctive style and charm. Floor-to-ceiling shelves are laden with well-sourced goodies from Britain and all over the world. The deli counter stocks a range of English hams, Italian and French salame, pâtés and fine artisan cheeses. You'll also find olives and award-winning pesto, pasties that really do come from Cornwall, a huge range of pasta and a good baby food section. Organic meat comes from Suffolk, and fresh bread is delivered daily. Husband prides herself on trying to source any product a customer requests.

Fishmonger

★ CONDON FISHMONGERS

363 Wandsworth Road, London SW8 2JJ
Tel: 020 7622 2934
Open: Tues, Wed, Fri and Sat 8.45am-5.30pm, Thurs 8.45am-1pm **Closed:** Mon, Sun, Bank holidays **Tube:** Stockwell **Bus:** 77, 77A, 322 **Mainline station:** Vauxhall **Payment:** cash, cheque

Don't let appearances deceive you. This unassuming shop supplies a steady stream of loyal customers. The Condon family business has been based in this shop since 1902, when the smokehouse commemorating Edward VII's coronation was built. It's still used every day, and shellfish is also boiled in the shop. The large selection of fresh fish (including Dover sole, monkfish, sea bass and turbot, the day we visited) is bought daily at Billingsgate Market, and oysters are imported directly from a supplier in Galway Bay on Ireland's west coast. If you are planning a seafood feast, Condon also lends fish kettles, fish plates, oyster knives and oyster plates – as well as selling you the main course!

MACFARLANE'S

48 Abbeville Road, London SW4 9NF
Tel: 020 8673 5373
Fax 020 8673 7744
Open: Mon–Fri 10am–7pm, Sat 9am–6pm, Sun 10am–5pm
Tube: Clapham South **Bus:** 155, 255, 355 **Payment:** cash, cheque, Delta, Maestro, MasterCard, Visa
Catering, delivery (organic vegetables only)

Angus MacFarlane and his wife, Angie, launched this wonderful little shop as a fromagerie in the late 1990s. But as their customers' requirements have changed, so, too, has MacFarlane's. Now, it's primarily a shop for people who love to cook, but 'don't have the time', explains Angus. Two large freezers are consequently packed with handmade frozen meals prepared by two local chefs, while the deli counter is well-stocked with fresh Machiavelli pasta, mozzarella delivered weekly from Naples, savoury pies and tarts, and Repertoire's additive- and colouring-free dips. You'll also find a wealth of store-cupboard staples directly sourced from small suppliers. There are unusual cheeses such as Glynhynod Farm's Teifi and Robin Congdon's Ticklemore, and up to 50 bread lines supplied by Millers, Il Mulino, Simply Bread and the nearby Lighthouse Bakery (page 176). Sweet tooths are also catered

Grocer
Delicatessen
Cheese Shop

for with a generous spread of Casemir chocolates (page 45) and Greyfriars' desserts, including tennis player Greg Rusedski's favourite banoffi pie. MacFarlane's comes through, too, when you're looking for that one elusive ingredient. 'If we haven't got it, we'll find it,' says Angus. The shop's note-covered back door, to which he's just added a request for crunchy peanut butter, proves he's a man of his word.

Butcher
Organic

M. MOEN & SONS

24 The Pavement,
London SW4 OJA
Tel: 020 7622 1624
Fax: 020 7622 1628
Website: www.moen.co.uk
Open: Mon-Fri 8.30am-6.30pm,
Sat 8am-5pm **Closed:** Sun, Bank holidays **Tube:** Clapham
Common **Bus:** 37, 88 **Mainline station:** Clapham High Street
Payment: cash, cheque, Delta, Maestro, MasterCard, Visa
Local delivery

More than just a butcher's shop, M. Moen & Sons sells everything from quail to bresaola. Organic and free-range pork, lamb and beef, plus prime Scottish beef, come from the Duke of Buccleuch's estates, and their quality is second to none. You'll also find 15 types of home-made sausages, cheeses including Denhay Farm's mature Cheddar and a wonderful selection of bread, including German dark rye, spelt bread and onion bread.

The shop also sells a small range of seasonal vegetables such as wild mushrooms, squashes and asparagus. You can buy all manner of goodies from the deli, including olives, artichokes, pestos, organic chutneys and marinades, and pâtés.

East Sheen

Chocolate

SANDRINE

239 Upper Richmond Road
West, London SW14 8QS
Tel: 020 8878 8168
Fax: 020 8744 9198
Website: www.sandrine.co.uk
Open: Mon-Sat 10am-5.30pm
Closed: Sun, Bank holidays
Mainline station: Mortlake **Bus:**
33, 337 **Payment:** cash, cheque,
Amex, Delta, Maestro,
MasterCard, Visa

Irish-born owner Jean Bradley's fine arts background is evident in Sandrine's beautiful, handmade packaging. Rightly proud of her stock, she specializes in handmade Belgian chocolates, many of which are made for her using only natural ingredients. Bradley also sells some English chocolates. In the summer, the fresh creams and fondants fly off of the shelves, while the pralines and truffles are popular during the winter months. Be sure to try the exquisite orange- and pistachio-flavoured marzipan, as well as the almond praline.

BUYING IN SEASON

Walking into any large supermarket today, shoppers are met with a huge array of fruit and vegetables, perfectly formed and neatly stacked in rows. Many of these will have been grown on the other side of the world and flown thousands of miles to get here, and so bear no relation to what is seasonally available. 'Progress' means that we can pretty much have whatever we want, whenever we want it. But at what cost? Locally grown foods, harvested and picked at their peak have infinitely more flavour than any of their supermarket counterparts. The first asparagus of the season is a joy worth waiting for, and autumn takes on its own special flavour with the arrival of freshly picked mushrooms. Here is a guide to what you should be buying through the year.

SPRING
Asparagus (cutting stops 21 June), beetroot, carrots, cauliflower, celery, cucumber, fennel, lamb, radishes, rhubarb, salmon, spinach, spring onions, turnips

SUMMER
Artichokes, berries, broad beans, cherries, courgettes, currants, early potatoes, French beans, gooseberries, leeks, new garlic, peas, runner beans, strawberries, raspberries, tomatoes

AUTUMN
Apples, blackberries, chard, corn on the cob, funghi, game, Jerusalem artichokes, Kent cobnuts, mushrooms, parsnips, pears, plums, pumpkins, squash

WINTER
Broccoli, Brussels sprouts, cabbage, celeriac, chicory, horseradish, onions, shallots, swedes, venison, watercress

Italian
Delicatessen
Grocer

★ **VALENTINA**
210 Upper Richmond Road West, London SW15 6TE
Tel: 020 8392 9127
Open: Mon-Fri 9am-7pm, Sat 8.30am-6pm, Sun, Bank holidays 9.30am-3pm **Closed:** 25, 26, Dec. **Mainline station:** Mortlake **Bus:** 33, R69, 337
Payment: cash, cheque, Amex, Delta, Maestro, MasterCard, Visa

Catering, food-to-go, free home delivery

Sergio Borfecchia established this popular, double-fronted

Italian emporium, which is named after his daughter, more than a decade ago. He stocks a wide range of hams, cheeses, salume, wines, grilled and marinated vegetables, and high-quality pâtés, but the highlights are his wife Anna's ready-made dishes. These might include *petti di pollo milanese*, cannelloni, lasagne, *melanzane parmigiana, frittata di zucchini*, stuffed peppers, roasted baby chickens and tiramisu – for which the shop is justly renowned You'll also find fresh roasted coffee, fresh pasta every day, sauces and ciabatta, plus home-made pizzas on Fridays and Saturdays. For Italian cooking with a twist, try the fresh (not cured) Parma ham roasted with herbs, or the boned and rolled pork flavoured with herbs. Bargain-hunters claim Valentina's white truffles are the cheapest in London.

Kew

Wholefoods
Organic
Grocer
Delicatessen

★ OLIVER'S WHOLEFOOD STORE

5 Station Approach, London TW9 3QB
Tel: 020 8948 3990
Open: Mon-Sat 9am-7pm, Sun 10am-7pm **Tube:** Kew Gardens **Bus:** 33, R69, 391 **Mainline station:** Kew Gardens **Payment:** cash, cheque, Delta, Maestro, MasterCard, Visa,

This excellent food shop, which now boasts its own natural therapy rooms next door, has been trading for more than a decade in the heart of Kew village. It is a mecca for high-quality, mostly organic produce of all kinds, as well as foods for those on special diets. Just beyond the front door, you are greeted with a huge display of fresh, organic fruit and vegetables. You'll also find organic ready-meals, fresh pasta and dips, freshly prepared salads, a wide selection of dairy produce, organic meats from Sheepdrove and Wootton, and fresh fish including haddock,

sardines, mackerel, herrings and Summer Isles organic, cured, smoked salmon. The shelves groan with organic items including herbs, spices, pulses, grains, dried fruit, sauces, vinegars, pasta, cakes, chocolates, coffee, preserves, herbal tea, oils, condiments, wines, spirits and much more. The bread – from soda bread to spelt sourdough – is supplied by Cranks, The Village Bakery, Paul (page 32), The Celtic Baker and other top-quality suppliers. At Christmas, Oliver's stocks free-range, organic geese and ducks, organic bronze turkeys and gammons and hams to order. The shop also boasts an extensive natural remedies and body care department, as well as a wide selection of books, magazines and other healthcare-related products. Most days, nutritionists and therapists are on hand to give dietary advice.

PETHER

16 Station Parade, Kew Gardens, Surrey TW9 3PZ
Tel: 020 8940 0163
Open: Mon-Fri 7am-6.30pm, Sat 7am-5pm **Closed:** Sun, Bank holidays **Tube:** Kew Gardens **Bus:** 33, R69, 391 **Mainline station:** Kew Gardens **Payment:** cash, cheque, Delta, Maestro, MasterCard, Visa

Butcher
Pies
Game dealer
Organic

There's been a butcher on this site for over 30 years and Pether, the latest occupant, is a fine example of the trade. Its pork pies and quiches are all home-made, as are the sausages, which include a scrumptious chilli and pork with leek and ginger variety. Service is friendly and knowledgeable, and Adrian Clemmy and Kevin Weston will happily prepare nine varieties of pie to order, including coq au vin and beef *bourguignon*.

Clemmy and Weston are also proud of their home-made chicken liver pâté, home-cooked ham and, somewhat incongruously, delicious chocolate mousse. Among the other temptations to be found here are organic and free-range chickens, free-range eggs, free-range turkeys at Christmas and Welsh and English lamb and geese. Nearly all of the beef is Aberdeen Angus and will have been hung for three weeks. In season, there is a good range of game, including grouse, partridge and pheasant. Pickles and chutneys, plus a 40-strong range of cheeses, are also on offer.

Putney

Italian
Delicatessen
Café

★ CARLUCCIO'S
The Brewhouse, Putney Wharf,
London SW15 2JQ
Tel: 020 8789 0591

Main shop: see Covent Garden,
page 28

★ MAISON BLANC
125 Putney High Street,
London SW15 1SU
Tel: 020 8789 6064

Main shop and branches: see
St John's Wood, page 132

★ TALAD THAI
326 Upper Richmond Road,
London SW15 6TL
Tel: 020 8789 8084
Fax: 020 8789 8601
Open: Mon-Sat 9am-8pm, Sun,
public holidays 10am-8pm
Closed: 25 Dec, 1 Jan **Tube:** East
Putney **Bus:** 337, 430 **Mainline
station:** Putney **Payment:** cash,
cheque, Amex, Delta,
MasterCard, Visa

This wonderful shop is a favourite of cookery writer Sri Owen. It may look rather unprepossessing from the outside, but it is well stocked with Thai and other Oriental ingredients. You'll find fresh fruit including mangoes, durian, mangosteen and bananas that are flown in from Thailand each week. There are also many varieties of Thai and Indian curry pastes, fish sauces, preserved fish, dried beans, noodles and tea, plus basics such as palm sugar, dried mushrooms, pickled greens and tamarind paste. The freezers are laden with spring roll pastry, fish and other seafood, and ready-to-cook food including dumplings, shrimp on sugar cane sticks and fish cakes. The open refrigerator carries a good

French Bakery
Pâtisserie

Thai
Delicatessen
Grocer

range of fresh Oriental greens, long beans, ready-prepared beef balls for soup, white aubergines, galangal, fresh tofu, beansprouts, rice noodles and the like. For keen cooks, the shop sells large, traditional mortars and pestles, and a selection of Oriental cookbooks. Demonstrations of Thai cooking are given at 11am most Sundays during the school term, and you can order take-away food from Talad Thai's restaurant, which is situated just two doors away, from 11am to 3pm and from 5.30pm to 10pm.

Richmond

French
Bakery
Pâtisserie

★ MAISON BLANC
27B The Quadrant,
London TW9 1DN
Tel: 020 8332 7041

Main shop and branches: see St John's Wood, page 132

Butcher
Game dealer
Organic

THE REAL BUTCHER
23 Friars Stile Road,
London TW10 6NH
Tel: 020 8940 0414
Open: Mon-Sat 7.30am-5.30pm

Closed: Sun, Bank holidays **Tube:** Richmond **Bus:** 33, 391, R69
Mainline station: Richmond
Payment: cash, cheque, Delta, Maestro, MasterCard, Visa

Steve Sains, the owner of this well-established butcher's shop, sells a range of groceries, although the core stock is meat and poultry, game in season, and frozen wild rabbit and venison all year. He and his friendly staff sell a good selection of home-made sausages, Greek-style marinated lamb for making *kleftiko* and marinated meats and poultry for summer barbecues. Bronze turkeys are a speciality at Christmas.

VIVIAN'S
2 Worple Way,
London TW10 6DF
Tel: 020 8940 3600
Open: Mon-Fri 9am-7pm, Sat 8am-6pm, Sun 8am-12pm
Closed: Bank holidays, Sun, Mon **Tube:** Richmond **Bus:** 33, 337, 371, R69 **Mainline station:** Richmond **Payment:** cash, cheque, Delta, Maestro, MasterCard, Visa
Catering, food-to-go

This gem of a shop, run by ex-chef and wine grower Richard Craig, enjoys an established customer base and a reputation for high-quality goods. Thanks to its knowledgeable and enthusiastic staff, it is a very pleasant place to visit. You are encouraged to try out the

Delicatessen

cheese and other fresh produce with no pressure to buy; and at weekends, you'll find an eclectic range of French wines freely available to taste. The shop's chef, Gabriel Peuget, makes the prepared foods upstairs. Typical *traiteur* meals include *boeuf bourgignon*, rabbit in mustard, paella, tortillas, home-made pâtés, terrines and, at Christmas, fresh foie gras. Phone in towards the weekend to check out the shop's Friday dinner-to-go specials. Everything else in the shop represents a foodie's wish list: there are 150 cheeses, many of which are British and unpasteurized; Hill Station ice cream; organic smoked salmon, trout, eel and ham; bread from Miller's Bespoke Bakery; a wide selection of roasted, preserved vegetables; extra virgin olive oils, some of which are available by the litre – bring your own bottle; sauces; vinegars; preserves; biscuits; and cakes. Christmas specialities include home-made puddings and cakes.

Roehampton

South African Butcher
Sausages
Grocer

ST. MARCUS FINE FOOD

1 Rockingham Close,
Priory Lane, off Upper
Richmond Road, London
SW15 5RW
Tel: 020 8878 1898
Fax: 020 8876 0761
Website:
www.stmarcus.equology.com
Open: Mon-Sun 9am-6pm **Tube:**

East Putney **Bus:** 10, 337 **Mainline station:** Barnes Common
Payment: cash, cheque, Delta, Maestro, MasterCard, Visa
Mail order

A member of the Guild of Master Butchers, this well-known South African butcher has been in situ for more than 22 years. Enter the shop and you are confronted with a forest of brownish-black stalactites hanging from the entire ceiling. These are, in fact, sticks of biltong (salted, dried ostrich, impala, kudu and beef meat that is a favourite with South Africans and is becoming increasingly popular in this country) in various stages of air-drying. You'll also find a range of high-quality meat and game including Scottish Aberdeen Angus beef and beef from Zimbabwe, plus springbok, wild boar and Scottish venison. The sosaties, flatties and gourmet sausages are specialities. More than 50 varieties of the latter are currently made on the premises, including eight types of boerwors. The deli section sells South African herbal tea, preserves, chutneys and tinned foods.

Streatham

KORONA DELICATESSEN

30 Streatham High Road,
London SW16 1DA
Tel: 020 8769 6647
Open: Mon-Fri 9am-7pm, Sat
9am-6pm, Sun 9am-3pm **Closed:**

Central
European
Delicatessen
Kosher

Bank holidays **Mainline station:** Streatham Hill **Bus:** 109, 118, 133, 159, 205 **Payment:** cash, cheque, Delta, Maestro, MasterCard, Visa

A Continental delicatessen has been at this site for more than 50 years, with the present, friendly Polish owners here since 1982. It's like the best of Eastern European delicatessens, with treats from Italy, Spain and South Africa thrown in as well. You'll find everything from salume, hams, sausages, jars of stuffed cabbage and *bigos* to Polish vodkas and spirits. The baked goods are abundant and authentic. Look out for German bread baked by Germans using German flour, Polish ryes and Ukrainian bread from Koles, the Ukrainian bakery in Bradford, plain and poppy seed cheesecakes, doughnuts biscuits and cakes. There is also a large kosher section, and a good range of Mediterranean specialities such as taramasalata and houmous. Fresh herbs are flown in from Italy.

Tooting

Butcher
Sausages

COPPIN BROTHERS
276 Mitcham Road,
London SW17 9NT
Tel: 020 8672 6053
Open: Tues-Sat 7am-4.30pm
Closed: Sun, Mon **Tube:** Tooting
Broadway **Bus:** 44, 77, 133, 155
Mainline station: Tooting
Junction **Payment:** cash, cheque,
Amex, Delta, MasterCard, Visa

Free local delivery

People come from far and wide to visit this traditional family butcher, which was founded over 100 years ago by James Coppin and is now run by his grandson. You'll find Aberdeen Angus beef, English lamb and wonderful hams; some of the meats are free-range. Home-cooked meats are prepared on the premises and include tongue, salt beef, roast beef and hams, for which the shop holds a clutch of gold awards. Coppin Brothers also makes its own sausages and has more than 10 varieties, including Cumberland, spicy tomato. What the shop is particularly famous for, however, is its Victorian Royal Roast, a boned goose stuffed with a boned pheasant, then a boned chicken and finally a boned quail. Service is friendly and the staff is always happy to offer advice.

DEEPAK FOODS
953-959 Garrett Lane,
London SW17 0LR
Tel: 020 8767 7819/7810
Fax: 020 8767 9002
Open: Mon-Sat 9am-8pm, Sun
10am-4pm **Tube:** Tooting
Broadway **Bus:** 77, 282 **Mainline
Station:** Tooting **Payment:** cash,
cheques, Delta, Maestro,
MasterCard, Visa

Resembling an Eastern bazaar inside, this large shop stocks an amazing array of foods and drinks from India and the Caribbeans,

Indian
Food Hall

plus produce from Europe. You will find every kind of dried pulse and a wide range of oils, butters, rice, flour and vegetable ghee. The selection of pastes, pickles and spices – including dried mixes for chicken masala, chicken passanda and ginger garlic – seems endless. The shop also has an in-store bakery, which produces French bread and pâtisserie. The frozen food section includes everything from halal lamb burgers, kofta kebabs, whole tilapia and king fish steaks to ready-made tagines. You'll also find a cornucopia of fresh vegetables including baby aubergines, long beans, sweet potatoes, yams, cassava and chow chow. Look out, too, for frozen fresh blackeye peas, pigeon peas, bitter melon and whole artichoke bottoms. The shop also stocks a wide and varied range of Indian bread.

NATURE FRESH
126-128 Upper Tooting Road, London SW17 7EN
Tel: 020 8682 4988
Open: Mon-Sun 8am-7pm **Tube:** Tooting Broadway **Bus:** 155, 219, 355 **Mainline station:** Tooting **Payment:** cash, cheque, Amex, Delta, Maestro, MasterCard, Visa

An impressive display of fresh fruit and vegetables is piled high at the front of this self-service greengrocer, where tomatoes, watermelons, garlic, chillies, custard apples, persimmons, mooli and huge bunches of fresh herbs fight for space. English, Afro-Caribbean and Asian communities are all catered for, and prices are competitive. Inside you can find an exhaustive range of *kulfi* (Indian ices), sugar cane, fresh tamarind, spices, biscuits and Asian bread.

Asian
Afro-Caribbean
Grocer
Greengrocer

Tooting Market and Broadway Market

Open: Mon, Tues, Thurs-Sat 9am-5.30pm, Wed 9am-1pm, **Tube:** Tooting Broadway
Bus: 155, 219, 355 **Mainline station:** Tooting

These two indoor markets are adjacent to each other on Upper Tooting Road, near Tooting Broadway tube station. You'll find excellent fishmongers offering familiar and unfamiliar seafoods, several vegetable and fruit stalls (with everyday and exotic produce), Afro-Caribbean groceries, halal and conventional butchers, and a multitude of household goods. There are some good snacks to be had in both markets, and fantastic food bargains at closing time on Saturdays.

Asian
Grocer

PATEL BROTHERS

187-191 Upper Tooting Road,
London SW17 7TG
Tel: 020 8767 6338/8672 2792
Open: Mon-Sat 8.30am-7pm,
Sun 9.30am-6pm **Tube:** Tooting
Broadway **Bus:** 155, 219, 355
Mainline station: Tooting
Payment: cash, cheque, Amex,
Delta, Maestro, MasterCard,
Visa

Patel Brothers claims to be the
first Asian grocery store in south
London, having been here since
1972. Local competition is now
hot, but the shop still seems to
offer what people want: an
enormous range of Indian and
Asian goods ranging from
pistachios to curry pastes, good-
quality hand-washed grains,
rices, beans and pulses. Most of
these can be bought in whatever
quantity is required, from a
400g pack to 32kg sacks, all
packed specially for Patel
Brothers, imported directly from
India and very good value. Look
out for the section of the store
that is given over to bulk goods,
where you can buy huge tins of
cashew kernels, oils of every sort
and sacks of flour and grain.
You'll also find fresh Asian
groceries such as turmeric roots,
baby aubergines, white radish,
spinach and fenugreek. There is
no doubt that the choice here can
be daunting. There are shelves
upon shelves of seasonings, spice
mixes, sauces, pickles, ready-to-make
snacks and tins of unusual fruit
and vegetables – but service is
friendly and there is always
someone who is willing to help
the uninitiated.

RAINBOW

201 Upper Tooting Road,
London SW17 7EN
Tel: 020 8672 7771
Open: Mon-Fri 9am-7pm, Sat
8.30am-6pm, Sun 9am-6pm
Tube: Tooting Broadway **Bus:**
155, 219, 355 **Mainline station:**
Tooting **Payment:** cash, cheque

Butcher
Fishmonger
Halal

The local Asian, Caribbean and
African communities crowd to
this meat, poultry and fish shop
in droves. Indeed, Saturdays
often see a long queue snaking
up the street. Behind the
counter, a sea of butchers in red
and white aprons weigh, cut,
chop and slice. The counter
display features mounds of
chicken wings and fresh goat
meat, steak and mutton. All all
the meat and fish is of high
quality and service is fast. The
prices are very keen, too.

New Covent Garden Market

Nine Elms Lane
Open: Mon-Fri 3am-11am, Sat 4am-10am **Closed:** 24 Dec.-5 Jan. **Tube:** Vauxhall
Bus: 2, 77, 77A, 88, 322, 344 **Mainline station:** Vauxhall
Fee: Cars visiting the market are charged £4 per visit **Website:** www.cgma.gov.uk

Now located at Nine Elms in Vauxhall, the famous wholesale market now houses some 300 companies in two principal buildings – the Fruit and Vegetable Market, with its annexe, the Pavilion, and the Flower Market. Some 70% of the food available is imported from abroad, so you can find almost anything in the world here in its season. This is primarily a wholesale market, but individuals are welcome as long as they buy in wholesale quantities – though this can be as little as a kilo of mushrooms. On Sundays, when the main market is closed, there is a small retail food market which offers meats, cheeses, eggs, bread and some fruit and vegetables.

Twickenham

Fishmonger
Poulterer
Game dealer
Grocer

★ SANDYS

56 King Street, Twickenham, Middlesex TW1 3SH
Tel: 020 8892 5788
Open: Mon-Sat 8am-6pm **Closed:** Sun, Bank holidays **Mainline station:** Twickenham **Bus:** 267, 281 **Payment:** cash, cheque, Delta, Maestro, MasterCard, Visa
Food-to-go

This immensely popular shop has been run by 'The Big Fella', Ray Sandys, for more than 15 years now. Specializing in seafood and game, it stocks a wide range of fresh fish and shellfish, as well as smoked salmon, trout, halibut, tuna, shark and marlin. On the day we visited, there was also Torbay sole and wild sea bass. In the refrigerators, you'll find Gressingham and Barbary ducks, fresh pigeon breast, whole guinea fowls, venison and wild boar, plus a range of home-made sausages. At Christmas, there are free-range geese and bronze turkeys; and for Hogmanay or Burns Night, the shop stocks the famous MacSweens haggis. If you are looking for something to go with your purchases, you'll find fresh herbs, sauces, preserves and mayonnaise, as well as organic cheeses and cream. Poached salmon and other fish are prepared to order for special occasions. Service is friendly and helpful.

Wimbledon

Delicatessen

BAYLEY & SAGE
60 High Street,
London SW19 5EE
Tel: 020 8946 9904
Tel: 020 8944 1138
Website: www.bayley-sage.co.uk
Open: Mon-Sun 8am-9pm **Tube:** Wimbledon **Bus:** 93, 200
Mainline station: Wimbledon
Payment: cash, cheques Amex, Delta, Maestro, MasterCard, Visa

Open since 1997, this friendly deli has established itself as the foodie's paradise of Wimbledon Village. Bayley & Sage prides itself on sourcing foods that come from local growers and farms, and are as natural and unprocessed as possible. At the heart of the store is a deli counter packed with more than a hundred British and European farmhouse cheeses. There's also some fabulous charcuterie, including salami and, when available, rare, acorn-fed Iberico ham. Look out, too, for the fresh, seasonal fruit and vegetables, and the bread sourced from 15 local suppliers, including Poilâne (page 19), Frankonia, The Bread Factory and Breads Etcetera. The meat chiller is crammed with 17 varieties of sausages, plus O'Doherty's traditional bacon and black pudding from Enniskillen. Elsewhere, you'll find a plethora of store-cupboard essentials, such as olive oils, single estate coffee from India and Brazil, pasta imported directly from Italy and a carefully chosen selection of wines such as Nyetimber's sparkling wine, Domaine Cordier's Pouilly Fume and McCashins' exquisite Sauvignon Blanc. At Christmas, the shop also stocks Copas Farms' top-notch free-range bronze turkeys and geese to order.

6 Farmers' markets give us the chance to sample the true taste of our local landscapes and rediscover the delights of regional food and drink. These bustling and vibrant markets provide fresh, nutritious, seasonal produce at its very best. 9

Hugh Fearnley-Whittingstall

Farmers' Markets

London's Farmers' Markets

London's first farmers' market opened in Islington in 1999 and now, several years on, they are springing up all over the capital. Their success can largely be attributed to one woman, Nina Planck, an American who saw the huge potential for making fresh, natural, nutritious food available to Londoners.

The idea is that farmers, growers and producers who are 'local' (in London that means within 100 miles of the M25) can sell their own fresh produce directly to the public. The National Association of Farmers' Markets has fairly strict guideines – strictly speaking, stallholders at a farmers' market have to be people who grow and sell their own produce in the locality ('No Middlemen!' is the motto) and they are not allowed to purchase and re-sell produce that isn't theirs.

The markets are popular with consumers for a number of reasons. Buyers can have access to truly fresh and seasonal produce. They can talk to the farmer about how the food is produced and how to cook it. More unusual crops can be grown, instead of the monocropping encouraged by large supermarkets. As a result, in many of the London markets you can now find seasonal produce such as striped beetroot, round carrots and pea shoots. As well as fruits and vegetables, goods include juices, cheeses, herbs, meats, fish and shellfish, wines, eggs and breads, and much more, some of it organic. But there are other benefits. Small local farmers and producers have a better chance of staying in business because they grow what they know their customers want. By reducing food miles (and therefore pollution), chemical preservatives and wasteful and environmentally unfriendly packaging, a healthier environment is created. Finally, farmers' markets build a strong sense of community, creating a vibrant atmosphere and livening up town and city centres. It's not only foodies from across town who turn up, but also pensioners and other locals, who like to talk to suppliers and growers, and to meet their neighbours at a set time each week.

The following is a list of Farmers' Markets operating in London. Times and locations can change and new markets are springing up all the time, so it is worth checking before you visit. A star indicates a market that operates within The National Association of Farmers' Markets criteria. For information on your area, contact:

LONDON FARMERS' MARKETS

PO Box 37363
London N1 7WB
Tel: 020 7704 9659
Fax: 020 7359 1938
E-mail: info@lfm.org.uk
Website: www.lfm.org.uk

NATIONAL ASSOCIATION OF FARMERS' MARKETS

PO Box 575
Southampton
SO15 7BZ
Tel: 0845 45 88 420
Website:
www.farmersmarkets.net

Central London

★ BARNES

Saturdays 1pm-4pm
Essex House, opposite the pond
Mainline Station: Barnes Bridge
Bus: 33, R69, 209

★ BELGRAVIA

Saturdays 9am-1pm
Junction of Pimlico Road and Ebury Street
Tube: Victoria, Sloane Square
Bus: C1

★ BLACKHEATH

Sundays 10am-2pm
Blackheath Station car park
Mainline station: Blackheath
Bus: 54, 89, 108, 202, 380

CHISWICK

Sundays 10am-2pm
Dukes Meadows, access via Edensor Road, off Great Chertsey Road
Mainline station: Chiswick
Bus: 237, 267, E3

★ EALING

Saturdays 9am-1pm
Leeland Road, West Ealing
Tube: Ealing Broadway
Bus: 83, 207, 208, 607, E8

★ ISLINGTON

Sundays 10am-2pm
Essex Road, opposite Islington Green
Tube: Angel
Bus: 38, 56, 73

★ MARYLEBONE

Sundays 10am-2pm
Cramer Street car park, just off Marylebone Hgh Street
Tube: Baker Street or Bond Street
Bus: 2, 13, 18, 27, 30, 74, 82, 113, 139, 189, 205, 274, 453

★ NOTTING HILL

Saturdays 9am-1pm
Car park behind Waterstones, access via

Kensington Place
Tube: Notting Hill Gate
Bus: 12, 27, 28, 52, 70, 94, 328

PARSONS GREEN
Saturdays 1pm-5pm
Lady Margaret School, access
through Irene Road
Tube: Parsons Green
Bus: 14, 28, 195

★ PECKHAM
Sundays 9.30am-1.30pm
Peckham Square, Peckham
High Street
Mainline station: Peckham
Rye or Queens Road
Bus: 12, 36, 171, 345

★ PIMLICO ROAD
Saturdays 9am-1pm
Orange Square, corner of
Pimlico Road and Ebury Street
Tube: Sloane Square
Bus: 11, 211, 239

PUTNEY
Fridays 11am-3pm
St Mary's Church, Putney
Bridge
Tube: Putney Bridge
Bus: 33, 337, 371, R69

★ STOKE NEWINGTON
Saturdays 10am-2.30pm
William Patten School, Stoke
Newington Church Street
Mainline station: Stoke
Newington
Bus: 73, 393, 476

★ SWISS COTTAGE
Wednesdays 10am-3pm
02 Centre Car Park, Finchley
Road, near Homebase

Tube: Swiss Cottage
Bus: 13, 82, 113, 187, 268,

Outer London

RICHMOND
Saturdays 11am-3pm
Heron Square, off Hill Street
Tube: Richmond
Mainline station: Richmond
Bus: 33, 65, 490, H22, H37,
R68, R70

★ TWICKENHAM
Saturdays 9am-1pm
Holly Road Car Park, Holly
Road, off King Street
Mainline station: Twickenham
Bus: 33, 490, H22, R68, R70

★ UXBRIDGE
Sundays 10am-2pm
Forecourt of Uxbridge Civic
Centre, High St, Uxbridge (free
parking in the Chimes shopping
centre)
Tube: Uxbridge
Bus: 207, 222, 331, A10, U1, U2

★ WHETSTONE
Fridays 11am-5pm
Whetstone High Road
(opposite Waitrose)
Tube: Totteridge & Whetstone
Bus: 34, 125, 234, 251, 263, 326

★ WIMBLEDON
Saturdays 9am-1pm
Wimbledon Park First School,
Havana Road
Tube: Wimbledon Park
Bus: 156

What indulgence to have a box of freshly picked, as Nature intended, vegetables, delivered to your doorstep every week.

Claire Phipps

Organic
Greengrocer

ABEL & COLE

Tel: 08452 62 62 62
e-mail: organics@abel-cole.co.uk
Website: www.abel-cole.co.uk
Open: Mon-Thurs 9am-7pm,
Fri 9am-6pm, 24-hour
answerphone **Closed:** Sat, Sun,
Bank holidays **Payment:** Delta,
Maestro, MasterCard, Visa
Minimum order: £6 for orders
not including meat or fish, £8
for orders including meat or fish
Delivery: Free

This pioneering organic food
delivery service catered only for
Londoners when it started in
1988, but now delivers across
the UK. The popular essential
organic vegetable box contains
eight seasonal varieties and
comes in various sizes to cater
for all households. In addition,
Abel & Cole supplies organic
meats, sustainably sourced fish,
dairy goods and freshly baked
bread from Brixton's The Old
Post Office Bakery. One-off
orders are accepted, but the
company prefers standing
orders, tailoring them to your
needs in terms of frequency
and content.

Chillies

COOL CHILE CO.

Tel: 0870 902 1145
Fax: 0870 162 3923
e-mail: dodie@coolchile.co.uk
Website: www.coolchile.co.uk
Open: Mon-Thurs 9.30am-
5.30pm, 24-hour answerphone
Payment: Delta, Electron, JCB,
Maestro, MasterCard, Solo,
Visa **Delivery:** £6 for Parcel
Force, £12.60 for Euro 48

Want to spice up meal times?
Dodie Miller is the person for
you. She imports an array of
dried chillies from Mexico and
can tell you everything there is
to know about them, from
which ones are the hottest or
mildest to how the flavours
vary. (The fainthearted should
look for the *choricero*, a no-heat
Spanish chile with a sweet
flavour, while the intrepid
should go for the *habanero*,
which is liable to blow your
head off.) She also sells meal
kits for the uninitiated, own-
range sauces and salsas,
authentic Mexican store-
cupboard ingredients such as
masa harina for making corn
tortillas and Mexican drinking
chocolate with cinnamon and
almonds, and kitchen
equipment including tortilla
presses and volcanic mortars
and pestles.

DELIVERANCE

Meal Delivery
Service

Tel: 0800 019 1111
Website: www.deliverance.co.uk
Open: All sites daily 4.30pm-
11pm, central London sites Sat
and Sun 11am-4.30pm, Mon-
Fri 10am-2.30pm
Payment: cash, Amex, Delta,
MasterCard, Visa, accounts
Minimum order: £12 **Delivery:** £2

This acclaimed food delivery
service offers a startling
selection of freshly cooked
meals, which can be delivered
to most areas of London within
45 minutes. It prides itself on
using only the best raw

ingredients and cooking everything from scratch at its kitchens, which are dotted around the capital. Choose from delicious salads – be sure to try Deliverance's own salad, which includes oven-crisped Parma ham, plum tomatoes, chicken and olives – and typically Italian, Japanese, Indian, Chinese and Thai dishes, desserts and drinks. The comprehensive menu caters for most tastes and is perfect for fast-living Londoners.

Italian
Delicatessen

ESPERYA
Tel: 00 800 280 52003
e-mail: info@esperya.com
Website: www.esperya.com
Open: Mon-Fri 8am-6pm
Payment: Amex, Diners Club, MasterCard, Visa **Minimum order:** 75 euros **Delivery:** Depends on weight of products ordered and delivery service

This Italian online shop is generally considered to be the king of food websites. Indeed, there isn't much you won't find on its product list. There are high-quality olive oils, vinegars, honeys, pasta, rice, meats, cheeses, seafood, fruit and veg, sweets, coffee and wines from every region of Italy. Everything is guaranteed to reach you in perfect condition, or Esperya will exchange it, replace it or refund your money.

FARMAROUND ORGANIC
Tel: 020 7627 8066
e-mail: homedelivery@farmaround.co.uk
Website: www.farmaround.co.uk
Open: Mon-Fri 9am-5.30pm, 24-hour answerphone **Closed:** Sat, Sun, Bank holidays
Payment: standing orders, Maestro, MasterCard, Visa
Minimum order: £10.55
Delivery: £1.00

Farmaround Organic delivers high-quality, organic produce throughout Greater London each week. You can choose from a wide range of fruit and veg bags that are designed to suit households of all sizes. The standard organic veg bag, for instance, contains nine varieties including potatoes, carrots, onions and – according to the season – leeks, tomatoes on the vine and French beans. All produce comes from 15 producers across England, plus a handful of others in Continental Europe. Along with the fruit and veg bags, you can also buy eggs, breads, honeys, pasta, olive oils and fruit juices.

THE FOOD FERRY
Tel: 020 7498 0827
Fax: 020 7498 8009
e-mail: e@foodferry.com
Website: www.foodferry.com
Open: phone Mon-Fri 8am-9pm, email Mon-Fri 8am-5pm
Closed: Sat, Sun, Bank holidays
Payment: Amex, Connect, Delta, Maestro, MasterCard, Visa **Delivery:** Depends on

Organic
Greengrocer
Grocer

Shopping
service

delivery time slot. Generally free for orders over £75, otherwise £4.25, plus an additional 50p for those in central London

This fabulous shopping service, known to fans as the 'ferry godmother' because it eliminates the drudgery of supermarket shopping, delivers fresh, organic groceries and everyday household items to your door – even if you live in a top floor flat. Its 3,500 items come from London's finest speciality delis and gourmet shops, and include free-range, organic meats, fresh fish from Billingsgate, Swaddles organic ready-meals, Poilâne bread (page 19) and The Food Ferry's own popular range of hampers. Place your order before 11am, and The Food Ferry can deliver the same evening.

Shopping
Service

FORMAN & FIELD
Tel: 020 8221 3939
Fax: 020 8221 3940
e-mail:
info@formanandfield.com
Web site:
www.formanandfield.com
Open: Mon-Fri 9am-5pm **Closed:** Sat, Sun **Payment:** Amex, Maestro, MasterCard, Visa
Minimum order: None
Delivery: £8.95

This fantastic shopping service sources all of its goods from award-winning British artisanal producers. H. Forman & Sons smoked fish – in particular its

London cure smoked salmon – is a great draw, as are that venerable institution's fresh and marinated fish and caviar. Forman & Field also stocks pâtés, pies and quiches from The Handmade Food Co. and Metfield Bakery, Pugh's Piglets lamb and pork, Denham's game and sausages, Alderton and Richard Woodall's ham, plus chutneys, sauces and preserves, wines and spirits, and its own range of cakes. As many items are produced to order, the company asks that you allow a minimum of seven working days to goods to be despatched.

THE FRESH FOOD CO.
Tel: 020 8749 8778
Fax: 020 8749 5936
e-mail:
organics@freshfood.co.uk
Website: www.freshfood.co.uk
Open: Mon-Fri 9am-6pm, 24-hour telephone **Payment:** Amex, Delta, Maestro, MasterCard, Visa **Minimum order:** £25 for meat orders **Delivery:** Included for fixed-price boxes, but £10 for meat and game orders that are not part of fixed-price boxes, and £8.50 for fish orders that are not part of fixed-price boxes and items ordered individually from the 'per kilo' price list

Since it launched in 1994, Josa and Thoby Young's nationwide, organic delivery service has won a clutch of awards, including the Soil Association's best National Organic Box Scheme, Best

Greengrocer
Organic
Grocer

Salad and Best Organic Internet Retailer awards. The company offers a wide range of organic fruit and veg, meat, fish, beer and wine boxes, to which you can add other goodies from the 'per kilo' list. Most popular is the organic produce box, which contains 6 to 9 kilograms of seasonal organic produce for £27.95. Regular weekly orders of this and the other 'fixed-price' boxes receive a 5% discount. Subscriptions can be changed at any time or cancelled with a week's notice.

Wholefood Organic

GOODNESS DIRECT

Tel: 0871 871 6611
Fax: 01327 301135
e-mail: info@goodnessdirect.co.uk
Website: www.goodnessdirect.co.uk
Open: Mon-Fri 8.30am-5pm, 24-hour answerphone **Closed:** Sat, Sun, Bank holidays **Payment:** Delta, JCB, Maestro, MasterCard, Solo, Visa **Minimum order:** Fresh produce orders must be over £15 **Delivery:** Free for online orders over £30 and mail-order, email and phone orders over £40. £3 charge for packing temperature-controlled boxes, and £6 charge for delivery of fresh produce

Goodness Direct launched as a retail concern in the 1980s, switched to wholesale in the 1990s and took over London-based Clearspring's mail-order business in 2003. It specializes in healthy and organic foods and supplies everything from organic vegetables, herbs and meats, sea-fresh fish and foods suitable for those with allergies or on special diets to groceries, household products and dietary supplements. It also carries a good range of Clearspring's organic, GM-free and Japanese foods.

GRAMMA'S

Tel: 020 8470 8751
Fax: 020 8548 8755
e-mail: info@grammasintl.com
Website: www.grammasintl.com
Open: Mon-Sat 9am-6pm
Closed: Sun **Payment:** cheque, postal order **Minimum order:** None **Delivery:** p&p

Afro-Caribbean Sauces

Drawing on the ancient Afro-Caribbean tradition of using chillies and spicy food to promote health benefits, Dounne Alexander started manufacturing a concentrated hot-pepper herbal sauce in 1987 as a tribute to her herbalist/spiritualist grandmother. Today, her range also includes concentrated herbal seasonings (with original, curry, Creole and hot-and-spicy flavours) and a selection of herbal tea and drinks. None of the products contains colourings, anti-caking agents, thickeners or fillers. They are also gluten- and yeast-free, and are suitable for anyone following a vegetarian or vegan diet.

Indian
Pickles

MRS BASSA'S INDIAN KITCHEN

Tel: 020 8543 7145
Fax: 020 8543 7194
e-mail: Mbikltd@aol.com
Website: www.mbik.co.uk
Open: Mon-Fri 10am-3pm
Closed: Sat, Sun, public holidays
Payment: cheque, Delta, Maestro, MasterCard, Switch, Visa **Minimum order:** Four jars
Delivery charge: £5.50 p&p

Whether you are settling down for a quick takeaway in front of TV, or have made your own curry, Mrs Bassa's condiments will give your meal an authentic touch. Made following Indian family recipes, with no artificial preservatives, colourings or additives, these dips, pickles, salsas and pastes couldn't be better if you were buying them in Delhi. The top-seller is garlic pickle, made with whole cloves. Other favourites include Prawn Balchow (prawns in a unique rich, spicy sauce) and a smooth paste of fresh green coriander and mint, just as delicious for a sandwich spread as for flavouring a chicken curry.

OLIVES ET AL

Olives
Delicatessen

Tel: 01258 474 300
Fax: 01258 474 301
e-mail: enquiries@olivesetal.co.uk
Website: www.olivesetal.co.uk
Open: Mon-Fri 8.30am-5.30pm
Payment: cheque, postal order, Maestro, MasterCard, Solo, Visa **Minimum order:** None
Delivery: Free for orders over £60.00, otherwise £4

This internet site was set up in 1992 by Annie and Giles Henschel, two foodies who were frustrated by the lack of good-quality olives available to buy in the UK. It stocks a wide range of marinated, smoked and speciality olives, along with other goodies including pedigree extra virgin olive oils, Balsamic vinegars, Tracklements sauces and divine kitchenware such as olive wood spoons, slate place mats and ceramic oil pourers. There are no artificial colours, flavourings or preservatives in the company's products and the packaging is minimal and elegant. Try the 'classic' jar of marinated and spicy Sicilian mixed olives in extra virgin olive oil with chilli, garlic, bay and black pepper.

THE ORGANIC DELIVERY COMPANY

Organic
Greengrocer

Tel: 020 7739 8181
e-mail: info@organicdelivery. co.uk
Website: www.organicdelivery.co.uk
Open: Mon-Fri 9am-5pm
Payment: Amex, Delta, Maestro, MasterCard, Visa **Order:** By 4pm day before delivery **Minimum order:** None **Delivery:** Free for orders

This Soil Association-registered company delivers a vast range of organic products in the London area (including Richmond, Teddington and Kingston). Each postcode has a delivery day, and The Organic

Delivery Company happily accepts both regular and one-off orders. Gluten-free, vegan and fair-trade products are available. The service also offers standard mixed organic fruit and vegetable boxes in small, medium and large sizes, plus everything else you might pick up on your weekly shop, bar meat and fish.

Spices
Herbs
Chillies

SEASONED PIONEERS

Tel: 0800 068 2348
Fax: 0151 709 9330
e-mail:
info@seasonedpioneers.co.uk
Website:
www.seasonedpioneers.co.uk
Open: Mon-Fri 9am-5pm **Closed:** Sat, Sun, Bank holidays
Payment: cheque, postal order, Maestro, MasterCard, Visa
Minimum order: None
Delivery: Free for orders over £15, otherwise £1.40

This Liverpool-based company (a sneaky inclusion in this book, but also a necessary one because it's so good) specializes in sourcing some of the world's most exotic herbs, chillies, spices and spice blends. Its products include naturally smoked Spanish *pimenton*, Middle Eastern sumac berries and Telicherry peppercorns from the Indian Malabar coast. The spice blends are all made to the company's own recipes.

Index

Page numbers in **bold** indicate a shop's main branch.

✱Denotes mail-order and delivery service only

Index

Index